BEYOND the HORIZON

A Beka Book® Pensacola, FL 32523-9100
a ministry of PENSACOLA CHRISTIAN COLLEGE

To Parents and Teachers

Youth is the period in life when the character of the individual is being formed. Students are eagerly searching for a workable sense of values. They need to see in the lives of great men and common men and in the lives of young people, such as they are, the unchanging values of the ages lived out. We need to give them through books, as well as through our lives and words, ideals to reach for and examples to follow.

If our country is to remain a land of liberty, we must continue to teach each individual to read and think on his own. Every school must not only teach students the basic skills of reading but also provide them with classroom practice in developing these reading skills throughout the upper grades. We cannot afford to allow any students to develop the attitude that others can do their reading for them, and thus their thinking also.

The stories in this reader have been selected from the readers of America's past and have been edited, modernized, and classroom-tested for student appeal and readability. This reader will introduce to children not only what is excellent in itself, but what their parents and grandparents have read before them—stories so good that they will never become old and stories that impart moral values.

Many values are taught throughout the book. Among them are honesty, integrity, courage, faith, kindness, industry, and patriotism.

Thought questions at the end of the stories greatly aid in the understanding and appreciation of the selections.

Beyond the Horizon

Staff Credits
Editors: Laurel Hicks, Heidi Mayfield, Shela Conrad, Debbie Beck
Designer: Stan Shimmin
Illustrators: Jason Atwell, John Ball, Joe Digangi, Kyle Henry, Jim Hutchinson,
    Brian Jekel, Chris Martinez, Jason Montgomery, Stan Shimmin

A Beka Book, a Christian textbook ministry of Pensacola Christian College, is designed to meet the need for Christian textbooks and teaching aids. The purpose of this publishing ministry is to help Christian schools reach children and young people for the Lord and train them in the Christian way of life.

Cataloging Data
Beyond the horizon / editor: Laurel Hicks . . .[et al.].
    p. ill. ; 28 cm. — [A Beka Book reading program]
    1. Readers. 2. Reading. I. Hicks, Laurel E.
(Laurel Elizabeth) II. A Beka Book, Inc.
Library of Congress: PE1119 .B49 1998 gr. 5
Dewey System: 428.6

Credits are on page 275 which is an extension of this copyright page.

Contents

UNIT 2

Hold on to America

*This story could be read during black history month.

UNIT 3

Missionary Call

Guide to Story Themes

This Is My Father's World

This Is My Father's World

Maltbie D. Babcock

This is my Father's world,
And to my list'ning ears
All nature sings, and round me rings
The music of the spheres.
This is my Father's world!
I rest me in the thought
Of rocks and trees, of skies and seas
His hand the wonders wrought.

This is my Father's world
The birds their carols raise;
The morning light, the lily white,
Declare their Maker's praise.
This is my Father's world!
He shines in all that's fair;
In the rustling grass I hear Him pass
He speaks to me ev'rywhere.

This is my Father's world
O let me ne'er forget
That tho' the wrong seems oft so strong
God is the Ruler yet.
This is my Father's world!
The battle is not done;
Jesus who died shall be satisfied,
And earth and heav'n be one.

The Trumpeter Swans

from The Trumpet of the Swan *by E. B. White*

In the spring of the year, nest-building is uppermost in a bird's mind: it is the most important thing there is. If she picks a good place, she stands a good chance of hatching her eggs and rearing her young. If she picks a poor place, she may fail to raise a family. The female swan knew this; she knew the decision she was making was extremely important.

The two swans first investigated the upper end of the pond, where a stream flowed slowly in. It was pleasant there, with reeds and bulrushes. Red-winged Blackbirds were busy nesting in this part of the pond, and a pair of Mallard Ducks were courting. Then the swans swam to the lower end of the pond, a marsh with woods on one side and a deer meadow on the other. It was lonely here. From one shore, a point of land

---

courting—*trying to win another's affection*

extended out into the pond. It was a sandy strip, like a little peninsula. And at the tip of it, a few feet out into the water, was a tiny island, hardly bigger than a dining table. One small tree grew on the island, and there were rocks and ferns and grasses.

"Take a look at this!" exclaimed the female, as she swam round and around.

"Ko-hoh!" replied her husband, who liked to have someone ask his advice.

The swan stepped cautiously out onto the island. The spot seemed made to order—just right for a nesting place. While the male swan floated close by, watching, she snooped about until she found a pleasant spot on the ground. She sat down, to see how it felt to be sitting there. She decided it was the right size for her body. It was nicely located, a couple of feet from the water's edge. Very convenient. She turned to her husband.

"What do you think?" she said.

"An ideal location!" he replied. "A perfect place! And I will tell you *why* it's a perfect place," he continued, majestically. "If an enemy—a fox or a coon or a coyote or a skunk—wanted to reach this spot with murder in his heart, he'd have to enter the water and get wet. And before he could enter the water, he'd have to walk the whole length of that point of land. And by that time we'd see him or hear him, and I would give him a hard time."

The male stretched out his great wings, eight feet from tip to tip, and gave the water a mighty clout to show his strength. This made him feel better right away. When a Trumpeter

clout—*a powerful blow*

4

Swan hits an enemy with his wing, it is like being hit by a baseball bat. A male swan, by the way, is called a "cob." No one knows why, but that's what he's called. A good many animals have special names: a male goose is called a gander, a male cow is called a bull, a male sheep is called a ram, a male chicken is called a rooster, and so on. Anyway, the thing to remember is that a male swan is called a cob.

The cob's wife pretended not to notice that her husband was showing off, but she saw it, all right, and she was proud of his strength and his courage. As husbands go, he was a good one.

The cob watched his beautiful wife sitting there on the tiny island. To his great joy, he saw her begin to turn slowly round and around, keeping always in the same spot, treading the mud and grass. She was making the first motions of nesting. First she squatted down in the place she had chosen. Then she twisted round and around, tamping the earth with her broad webbed feet, hollowing it out to make it like a saucer. Then she reached out and pulled twigs and grasses toward her and dropped them at her sides and under her tail, shaping the nest to her body.

The cob floated close to his mate. He studied every move she made.

"Now another medium-sized stick, my love," he said. And she poked her splendid long white graceful neck as far as it would go, picked up a stick, and placed it at her side.

"Now another bit of coarse grass," said the cob, with great dignity.

The female reached for grasses, for moss, for twigs— anything that was handy. Slowly, carefully, she built up the nest until she was sitting on a big grassy mound. She worked at the task for a couple of hours, then knocked off for the day and slid into the pond again to take a drink and have lunch.

"A fine start!" said the cob, as he gazed back at the nest. "A perfect beginning! I don't know how you manage it so cleverly."

"It comes naturally," replied his wife. "There's a lot of work to it, but on the whole it is pleasant work."

"Yes," said the cob. "And when you're done, you have something to show for your trouble—you have a swan's nest, six feet across. What other bird can say that?"

"Well," said his wife, "maybe an eagle can say it."

"Yes, but in that case it wouldn't be a swan's nest, it would be an eagle's nest, and it would be high up in some old dead tree somewhere, instead of right down near the water, with all the conveniences that go with water."

They both laughed at this. Then they began trumpeting and splashing and scooping up water and throwing it on their backs, darting about as though they had suddenly gone crazy with delight.

"Ko-hoh! Ko-hoh! Ko-hoh!" they cried.

Every wild creature within a mile and a half of the pond heard the trumpeting of the swans. The fox heard, the raccoon heard, the skunk heard. One pair of ears heard that did not belong to a wild creature. But the swans did not know that.

One day, almost a week later, the swan slipped quietly into her nest and laid an egg. Each day she tried to deposit one egg in the nest. Sometimes she succeeded, sometimes she didn't. There were now three eggs, and she was ready to lay a fourth.

As she sat there, with her husband, the cob, floating gracefully nearby, she had a strange feeling that she was being watched. It made her uneasy. Birds don't like to be stared at. They particularly dislike being stared at when they are on a nest. So the swan twisted and turned and peered everywhere. She gazed intently at the point of land that jutted out into the pond near the nest. With her sharp eyes, she searched the nearby shore for signs of an intruder. What she finally saw gave her the surprise of her life. There, seated on a log on the point of land, was a small boy. He was being very quiet, and he had no gun.

"Do you see what I see?" the swan whispered to her husband.

"No. What?"

"Over there. On that log. It's a boy! *Now* what are we going to do?"

"How did a boy get here?" whispered the cob. "We are deep in the wilds of Canada. There are no human beings for miles around."

"That's what I thought too," she replied. "But if that isn't a boy over there on that log, my name isn't Cygnus Buccinator."

The cob was furious. "I didn't fly all the way north into Canada to get involved with a *boy*," he said. "We came here to this idyllic spot, this remote little hideaway, so we could enjoy some well-deserved privacy."

"Well," said his wife, "I'm sorry to see the boy, too, but I must say he's behaving himself. He sees us, but he's not throwing stones. He's not throwing sticks. He's not messing around. He's simply observing."

"I do not *wish* to be observed," complained the cob. "I did not travel all this immense distance into the heart of Canada to be observed. Furthermore, I don't want *you* to be observed—except by me. You're laying an egg—that is, I *hope* you are—and you are entitled to privacy. It has been my experience that all boys throw stones and sticks—it is their nature. I'm going over and strike that boy with my powerful wing, and he'll think he has been hit with a billy club. I'll knock him cold!"

"Now, just wait a minute!" said the swan. "There's no use starting a fight. This boy is not bothering me at the moment. He's not bothering you either."

Cygnus Buccinator (sĭg′nəs byo͞o′sĭn·ā·tôr)
idyllic—*simple*
billy club—*a short, thick stick carried for protection*

8

"But how did he *get* here?" said the cob, who was no longer talking in a whisper but was beginning to shout. "How did he get here? Boys can't fly, and there are no roads in this part of Canada. We're fifty miles from the nearest highway."

"Maybe he's lost," said the swan. "Maybe he's starving to death. Maybe he wants to rob the nest and eat the eggs, but I doubt it. He doesn't look hungry. Anyway, I've started this nest, and I have three beautiful eggs, and the boy's behaving himself at the moment, and I intend to go right ahead and try for a fourth egg."

"Good luck, my love!" said the cob. "I shall be here at your side to defend you if anything happens. Lay the egg!"

For the next hour, the cob paddled slowly round and around the tiny island, keeping watch. His wife remained quietly on the nest. Sam sat on his log, hardly moving a muscle. He was spellbound at the sight of the swans. They were the biggest water birds he had ever seen. He had heard their trumpeting and had searched the woods and swamps until he had found the pond and located the nest. Sam knew enough about birds to know that these were Trumpeters. Sam always felt happy when he was in a wild place among wild creatures. Sitting on his log, watching the swans, he had the same good feeling some people get when they are sitting in church.

After he had watched for an hour, Sam got up. He walked slowly and quietly away, putting one foot straight ahead of the other, Indian-fashion, hardly making a sound. The swans watched him go. When the female left the nest, she turned and looked back. There, lying safely in the soft feathers at the

bottom of the nest, was the fourth egg. The cob waddled out onto the island and looked in the nest.

"A masterpiece!" he said. "An egg of supreme beauty and perfect proportions. I would say that that egg is almost five inches in length."

His wife was pleased.

When the swan had laid five eggs, she felt satisfied. She gazed at them proudly. Then she settled herself on the nest to keep her eggs warm. Carefully, she reached down with her bill and poked each egg until it was in just the right spot to receive the heat from her body. The cob cruised around close by, to keep her company and protect her from enemies. He knew that a fox prowled somewhere in the woods; he had heard him barking on nights when the hunting was good.

Days passed, and still the swan sat quietly on the five eggs. Nights passed. She sat and sat, giving her warmth to the eggs. No one disturbed her. The boy was gone—perhaps he would never come back. Inside of each egg, something was happening that she couldn't see: a little swan was taking shape. As the weeks went by, the days grew longer, the nights grew shorter. When a rainy day came, the swan just sat still and let it rain.

"My dear," said her husband, the cob, one afternoon, "do you never find your duties onerous or irksome? Do you never tire of sitting in one place and in one position, covering the eggs, with no diversions, no pleasures, no escapades, or capers? Do you never suffer from boredom?"

"No," replied his wife. "Not really."

"Isn't it uncomfortable to sit on eggs?"

"Yes it is," replied the wife. "But I can put up with a certain amount of discomfort for the sake of bringing young swans into the world."

"Do you know how many more days you must sit?" he asked.

"Haven't any idea," she said. "But I notice that the ducks at the other end of the pond have hatched their young ones; I noticed that the Red-winged Blackbirds have hatched theirs, and the other evening I saw a Striped Skunk hunting along the shore, and she had four little skunks with her. So I think I must be getting near the end of my time. With any luck, we will soon be able to see our children—our beautiful little cygnets."

"Don't you ever feel the pangs of hunger or suffer the tortures of thirst?" asked the cob.

"Yes, I do," said his mate. "As a matter of fact, I could use a drink right now."

The afternoon was warm; the sun was bright. The swan decided she could safely leave her eggs for a few minutes. She stood up. First she pushed some loose feathers around the

---

onerous—*troublesome*
irksome—*annoying*
escapades—*adventures*
capers—*playful acts*
cygnets—*baby swans*

eggs, hiding them from view and giving them a warm covering in her absence. Then she stepped off the nest and entered
the water. She took several quick drinks. Then she glided
over to a shallow place, thrust her head underwater, and
pulled up tender greens from the bottom. She next took a
bath by tossing water over herself. Then she waddled out
onto a grassy bank and stood there, preening her feathers.

The swan felt good. She had no idea that an enemy was
near. She failed to notice the Red Fox as he watched her from
his hiding place behind a clump of bushes. The fox had been
attracted to the pond by the sound of splashing water. He
hoped he would find a goose. Now he sniffed the air and
smelled the swan. Her back was turned, so he began creeping
slowly toward her. She would be too big for him to carry, but
he decided he would kill her anyway and get a taste of blood.
The cob, her husband, was still floating on the pond. He
spied the fox first.

"Look out!" he trumpeted. "Look out for the fox, who is
creeping toward you even as I speak, his eyes bright, his
bushy tail out straight, his mind lusting for blood, his belly
almost touching the ground! You are in grave danger, and we
must act immediately."

While the cob was making this elegant speech of warning,
something happened that surprised everybody. Just as the
fox was about to spring and sink his teeth in the swan's neck,
a stick came hurtling through the air. It struck the fox full on
the nose, and he turned and ran away. The two swans
couldn't imagine what had happened. Then they noticed a
movement in the bushes. Out stepped Sam Beaver, the boy
who had visited them a month ago. Sam was grinning. In his

hand he held another stick, in case the fox should return. But the fox was in no mood to return. He had a very sore nose, and he had lost his appetite for fresh swan.

"Hello," said Sam in a low voice.

"Ko-hoh, ko-hoh!" replied the cob.

"Ko-hoh!" said his wife. The pond rang with the trumpet sounds—sounds of triumph over the fox, sounds of victory and gladness.

Sam was thrilled at the noise of swans, which some people say is like the sound of a French horn. He walked slowly around the shore to the little point of land near the island and sat down on his log. The swans now realized, beyond any doubt, that the boy was their friend. He had saved the swan's life. He had been in the right place at the right time and with the right ammunition. The swans felt grateful. The cob swam over toward Sam, climbed out of the pond, and stood close to the boy, looking at him in a friendly way and arching his neck gracefully. Once, he ran his neck far out, cautiously, and almost touched the boy. Sam never moved a muscle. His heart thumped from excitement and joy.

The female paddled back to her nest and returned to the job of warming the eggs. She felt lucky to be alive.

That night before Sam crawled into his bunk at camp, he got out his notebook and found a pencil. This is what he wrote:

> I don't know of anything in the entire world more wonderful to look at than a nest with eggs in it. An egg, because it contains life, is the most perfect thing there is. It is beautiful and mysterious. An egg is a far finer thing than a tennis ball or a cake of soap. A tennis ball will always be just a tennis ball. A cake of soap will always be just a cake

of soap—until it gets so small nobody wants it and they throw it away. But an egg will someday be a living creature. A swan's egg will open and out will come a little swan. A nest is almost as wonderful and mysterious as an egg. How does a bird know how to make a nest? Nobody ever taught her. How does a bird know how to build a nest?

Sam closed his notebook, said good night to his father, blew out his lamp, and climbed into his bunk. He lay there wondering how a bird knows how to build a nest. Pretty soon his eyes closed, and he was asleep.

You will want to read E. B. White's classic book, *The Trumpet of the Swan*, for further adventures of the Swan family.

Time to Think

1. What is a male swan called?
2. What made the island a perfect place for the swan's nest?
3. Who did the swans discover was watching them?
4. How did Sam prove to the swans that he could be trusted?

All Nature Sings

Phyllis C. Michael

All nature sings her song of praise,
She shows her thanks in many ways;
Can I, for all God's gifts do less
Than sing my hymn of gratefulness?

The brook which gaily babbles on
Sings day and night her cheerful song;
She sings her praise to God on high
For grandeur which she passes by.

The joyous song of tall pine trees
Through soft caress of evening breeze
Sends forth true thanks for constant love
For constant blessing from above.

The tulip stretches forth its cup,
The lowly shrubs turn branches up;
They, too, would faithful homage pay
By speaking in their faultless way.

---

homage—*special honor and respect*

The peaceful drone of lowing herds,
The clear, sweet tones of singing birds
Each thank the God who never sleeps
For ev'ry loving watch He keeps.

    The valleys fair, the purple hills,
    The mountain rocks, the spring that fills,
    All silently show forth His care
    Whose love and power is everywhere.

        The springtime buds, the autumn glow,
        The summer rain, the winter snow,
        All speak of His protecting hand,
        All say, "'Twas wisely, safely planned."

---

drone—*a low continuous sound*

Children of the Wind
Carl Sandburg

On the shores of Lake Michigan
high on a wooden pole, in a box,
two purple martins had a home,
and taken away down to Martinique
and let loose, they flew home,
thousands of miles to be home again.

The birds let out began flying
north, north-by-west, north,
till they were back home.
How their instruments told them
of ceiling, temperature, air pressure,
how their control-boards gave them
reports of fuel, ignition, speeds,
is out of the record, out.

Across spaces of sun and cloud,
in rain and fog, through air pockets,
wind with them, wind against them,
stopping for subsistence rations,
whirling in gust and spiral,
these people of the air,
these children of the wind,
had a sense of where to go and how,
how to go north, north-by-west, north,
till they came to one wooden pole,
till they were home again.

Martinique (mär′tə·nēk′)—*an island
  in the West Indies*
ceiling—*the maximum height at which one
  can fly under normal conditions*
subsistence rations—*just enough food to stay alive*

18

Bambi Makes Friends

Felix Salten

One evening Bambi was roaming about the meadow again with his mother. He thought that he knew everything there was to see or hear there. But in reality it appeared that he did not know as much as he thought.

This time was just like the first. Bambi played tag with his mother. He ran around in circles, and the open space, the deep sky, the fresh air intoxicated him so that he grew perfectly wild. After a while he noticed that his mother was standing still. He stopped short in the middle of a leap so suddenly that his four legs spread far apart. To get his balance he bounded high into the air and then stood erect. His mother seemed to be talking to someone he couldn't make out through the tall grasses. Bambi toddled up inquisitively.

Two long ears were moving in the tangled grass stems close to his mother. They were grayish brown and prettily marked with black stripes. Bambi stopped, but his mother said, "Come here. This is our friend, the Hare. Come here like a nice boy and let him see you."

intoxicated—*excited*

Bambi went over. There sat the Hare looking like a very honest creature. At times his long spoonlike ears stood bolt upright. At others they fell back limply as though they had suddenly grown weak. Bambi became somewhat critical as he looked at the whiskers that stood out so stiff and straight on both sides of the Hare's mouth. But he noticed that the Hare had a very mild face and extremely good-natured features and that he cast timid glances at the world from out of his big round eyes. The Hare really did look friendly. Bambi's passing doubts vanished immediately. But oddly enough, he had lost all the respect he originally felt for the Hare.

"Good evening, young man," the Hare greeted him, with studied politeness.

Bambi merely nodded good evening. He didn't understand why, but he simply nodded. He was very friendly and civil, but a little condescending. He could not help himself. Perhaps he was born that way.

"What a charming young prince," said the Hare to Bambi's mother. He looked at Bambi attentively, raising first one spoonlike ear, then the other, and then both of them, and letting them fall again, suddenly and limply, which didn't please Bambi. The motion of the Hare's ears seemed to say, "He isn't worth bothering with."

Meanwhile the Hare continued to study Bambi with his big round eyes. His nose and his mouth with the handsome whiskers moved incessantly in the same way a man who is trying not to sneeze twitches his nose and lips. Bambi had to laugh.

---

studied—*learned and thought about*
civil—*polite and socially acceptable*
condescending—*having an air of superiority*
incessantly—*without stopping*

The Hare laughed quickly, too, but his eyes grew more thoughtful. "I congratulate you," he said to Bambi's mother. "I sincerely congratulate you on your son. Yes, indeed, he'll make a splendid prince in time. Anyone can see that."

To Bambi's boundless surprise he suddenly sat straight on his hind legs. After he had spied all around with his ears stiffened and his nose constantly twitching, he sat down decently on all fours again. "Now if you good people will excuse me," he said at last, "I have all kinds of things to do tonight. If you'll be so good as to excuse me...." He turned away and hopped off with his ears back so that they touched his shoulders.

"Good evening," Bambi called after him.

His mother smiled. "The good Hare," she said; "he is so suave and prudent. He doesn't have an easy time of it in this world." There was sympathy in her voice.

Bambi strolled about a little and left his mother to her meal. He wanted to meet his friend again and he wanted to make new acquaintances, besides. For without being very clear himself what it was he wanted, he felt a certain expectancy. Suddenly, at a distance, he heard a soft rustling on the meadow, and felt a quick, gentle step tapping the ground. He peered ahead of him. Over on the edge of the woods something was gliding through the grasses. Was it alive? No, there were two things. Bambi cast a quick glance at his mother but she wasn't paying attention to anything and had her head deep in the grass. But the game was going on on the other side of the meadow in a shifting circle exactly as Bambi himself had raced around before. Bambi was so excited that he sprang back as if he wanted to run away. Then his mother noticed him and raised her head.

"What's the matter?" she called.

suave—*agreeable*
prudent—*having common sense; practical*

But Bambi was speechless. He could not find his tongue and only stammered, "Look over there."

His mother looked over. "I see," she said, "that's my sister, and sure enough she has a baby too, now. No, she has two of them." His mother spoke at first out of pure happiness, but she had grown serious. "To think that Ena has two babies," she said, "two of them."

Bambi stood gazing across the meadow. He saw a creature that looked just like his mother. He hadn't even noticed her before. He saw that the grasses were being shaken in a double circle, but only a pair of reddish backs were visible like thin red streaks.

"Come," his mother said, "we'll go over. They'll be company for you."

Bambi would have run, but as his mother walked slowly, peering to right and to left at every step, he held himself back. Still, he was bursting with excitement and very impatient.

"I thought we would meet Ena sometime," his mother went on to say. "Where can she have been keeping herself? I thought I knew she had one child, that wasn't hard to guess. But two of them! . . ."

At last the others saw them and came to meet them. Bambi had to greet his aunt, but his mind was entirely on the children.

His aunt was very friendly. "Well," she said to him, "this is Gobo and that is Faline. Now you run along and play together."

The children stood stock-still and stared at each other, Gobo close beside Faline and Bambi in front of him. None of them stirred. They stood and gaped.

---

gaped—*stared with an open mouth*

23

"Run along," said Bambi's mother, "you'll soon be friends."

"What a lovely child," Aunt Ena replied. "He is really lovely. So strong, and he stands so well."

"Oh well," said his mother modestly, "we have to be content. But to have two of them, Ena! . . ."

"Oh yes, that's all very well," Ena declared; "you know, dear, I've had children before."

"Bambi's my first," his mother said.

"We'll see," Ena comforted her, "perhaps it will be different with you next time, too."

The children were still standing and staring at each other. No one said a word. Suddenly Faline gave a leap and rushed away. It had become too much for her.

In a moment Bambi darted after her. Gobo followed him. They flew around in a semicircle, they turned tail and fell over each other. Then they chased each other up and down. It was glorious. When they stopped, all topsy-turvy and somewhat breathless, they were already good friends. They began to chatter.

Bambi told them how he talked to the nice grasshopper and the butterfly.

"Did you ever talk to the goldbug?" asked Faline.

No, Bambi had never talked to the goldbug. He did not even know who he was.

"I've talked to him often," Faline declared, a little pertly.

"The jay insulted me," said Bambi.

"Really," said Gobo astonished, "did the jay treat you like that?" Gobo was very easily astonished and was extremely timid.

---

goldbug—*a beetle having a gold color*

"Well," he observed, "the hedgehog stuck me in the nose." But he only mentioned it in passing.

"Who is the hedgehog?" Bambi asked eagerly. It seemed wonderful to him to be there with friends, listening to so many exciting things.

"The hedgehog is a terrible creature," cried Faline, "full of long spines all over his body and very wicked!"

"Do you really think he's wicked?" asked Gobo. "He never hurts anybody."

"Isn't that so?" answered Faline quickly. "Didn't he stick you?"

"Oh, that was only because I wanted to speak to him," Gobo replied, "and only a little anyhow. It didn't hurt me too much."

Bambi turned to Gobo. "Why didn't he want you to talk to him?" he asked.

"He doesn't talk to anybody," Faline interrupted; "even if you just come where he is he rolls himself up so he's nothing but prickles all over. Our mother says he's one of those people who don't want to have anything to do with the world."

"Maybe he's only afraid," Gobo said.

But Faline knew better. "Mother says you shouldn't meddle with such people," she said.

Presently Bambi began to ask Gobo softly, "Do you know what 'danger' means?"

Then they both grew serious and all three heads drew together. Gobo thought a while. He made a special effort to

---

hedgehog—*a small animal similar to a porcupine*

remember for he saw how curious Bambi was for the answer. "Danger," he whispered, "is something very bad."

"Yes," Bambi declared excitedly, "I know it's something very bad, but what?" All three trembled with fear.

Suddenly Faline cried out loudly and joyfully, "I know what danger is—it's what you run away from." She sprang away. She couldn't bear to stay there any longer and be frightened. In an instant, Bambi and Gobo had bounded after her. They began to play again. They tumbled in the rustling, silky green meadow grass and in a twinkling had forgotten all about the absorbing question.

Bambi is a classic book that everyone should read.

He hath made every thing
beautiful in His time.
—*Ecclesiastes 3:11*

Time To Think

1. Why did Bambi laugh when he met the Hare?
2. How were Gobo and Faline related to Bambi?
3. Why didn't the three fawns know what danger was?
4. Describe Faline.

Meeting

Rachel Field

As I went home on the old wood road,
   With my basket and lesson book,
A deer came out of the tall trees
   And down to drink at the brook.

Twilight was all about us,
   Twilight and tree on tree;
I looked straight into its great, strange eyes
   And the deer looked back at me.

Beautiful, brown, and unafraid,
   Those eyes returned my stare,
And something with neither sound nor name
   Passed between us there.

Something I shall not forget;
   Something still, and shy, and wise,
In the dimness of the woods,
   From a pair of gold-flecked eyes.

Smells
Kathryn Worth

Through all the frozen winter
My nose has grown most lonely
For lovely, lovely, colored smells
That come in springtime only.

The purple smell of lilacs,
The yellow smell that blows
Across the air of meadows
Where bright forsythia grows.

The tall pink smell of peach trees,
The low white smell of clover,
And everywhere the great green smell
Of grass the whole world over.

---

forsythia—*yellow flowers*

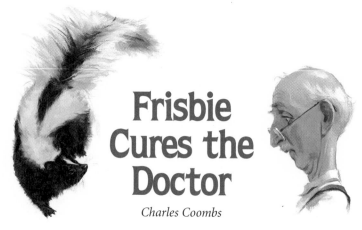

Frisbie Cures the Doctor

Charles Coombs

Lem Burgin is usually as cheerful as a cat in a salmon cannery. But on that particular morning, when he came to the back door in answer to my call, I could see trouble written all over his freckled face.

"Lem," I said, "it can't be *that* bad."

"It—it's Frisbie," he said solemnly.

"You mean he has disappeared? Run away?" I'm afraid I wasn't very careful at hiding the hope in my voice.

"Frisbie is ill," Lem explained.

"And I suppose you walked the floor all night with a sick skunk," I scoffed.

"It might be serious, Ned," he said. "Come on in and have a look at him."

"You've got him in the house?"

"Why not?"

"Thanks, but I think I'll stay out here where a guy has a fifty-fifty chance of making a clean break, should Frisbie become incensed at something."

"Have it your way," Lem said. "But someday you'll learn to appreciate Frisbie."

---

cannery—*a factory where food is put into cans*
incensed—*very angry*

30

"Don't hold your breath. On second thought, it's a good idea, when you're around Frisbie."

Lem went back into the house, letting my humor pass unheeded. Quickly he came back carrying an apple box. I eased cautiously to windward as Lem set the box on the lawn.

"Come on, Ned," Lem said impatiently. "He's not going to bite you!"

"Look, pal, I've never been worried about Frisbie biting me."

I moved in closer, then. I wasn't really as afraid of Frisbie as I let on. After all, we had been through quite a few adventures together, Lem, Frisbie, and I. And, as yet, neither Lem nor I had to bury any clothes. Still, I never wanted to be caught off guard.

Well, Frisbie did look somewhat peaked, at that. He turned his shoe-button eyes up toward us. His teeth were making a sort of clicking sound. I'll admit I was somewhat moved by the poor little fellow's sad appearance.

"Skunk fever," I said professionally.

"No, I think he has a sticker in his ear," Lem corrected. "Notice how he holds his head over to one side. See the swelling? Look close, Ned."

Well, maybe I was moved, but not that close.

"We've got to take him to a doctor," Lem said.

"A doctor! Lem, you're the guy to take to a doctor, if you think anyone would let you within a block of his office with Frisbie."

"There's Doctor Boland down on Cypress Street. He's a veterinarian."

"Cats and dogs," I reminded him.

"A good veterinarian should know about all animals."

"Even skunks?"

"Skunks are animals. Come on. That sticker or whatever it is may be working its way toward Frisbie's brain!"

"Skunks don't need brains," I said, but I fell in beside him as he started toward town. "You know, Lem, Doc Boland has the reputation of being very high priced, even for treating far less complicated animals."

But Lem's sense of economy was blinded by his love for Frisbie. He didn't answer.

We arrived at the white stucco building which housed Doc Boland's dog-and-cat hospital. The barking of dogs and the meowing of cats filtered through the partition that sepa-

---

stucco—*thick plaster*

rated the waiting room from the rest of the building. We waited and made sufficient noise to attract anyone's attention who might be in the back room. Still, no one showed up.

"Bolands live in a house in the rear," I said. "Maybe the doctor's eating lunch. Let's go see."

We found him back there, all right. He was an elderly man, not given much to smiling. He had a fringe of white hair that formed a windbreak around a patch of arid scalp. He peered out at us over his bifocals.

"What's on your minds, boys?" he said. "If you had gone into the office, I'd have known you were here."

"We did go inside," I said.

"You did? Then that buzzer must be out of order again." He pointed to the wire that ran back from the hospital and disappeared into a small square box under the porch eaves. "Well, anyway—here, Myra," he spoke to the little three- or four-year-old girl who had been sitting on his lap, "you'd better get down now so I can see what these boys want. My granddaughter," he explained proudly.

"She sure is cute," I said, cootcheecooing her under the chin, then watching her run pell-mell around the house. Always good business to get in solid with the kids, I thought. Might help Lem when the bills were written.

"I—I have a sick animal here, Doctor Boland." Lem suddenly came to life.

"Well, you've come to the right place. Must be a small one. Let's have a look in that box, and—whoa! Hey, what kind of a joke—get that thing out of here!"

---

arid—*dry*
pell-mell—*in a frantic, confused manner*

Well, I think Lem could have stood anything but to have a man whose profession is animals take such a sudden offense at Frisbie. The look of disillusionment that cast a cloud over Lem's face was pretty awful to behold. As for me, I was never one to defend Frisbie. In fact, Frisbie had never needed help. But this was different, somehow.

"Lem's skunk is friendly and tame, Doctor Boland," I said quickly, quite astounded at the sound of my own words. "And he's ill. Even a sick skunk deserves some sort of care."

"Not by me." Doctor Boland stood adamant with his back to the wall. "Take him to the dog pound or the city incinerator, or—"

That was dangerous talk for anybody, with Lem around. And the very fact that he didn't challenge Doctor Boland's thoughtless remark convinced me of just how concerned Lem was over Frisbie's health.

"I—I'll pay you whatever you ask," Lem said in a sort of choking voice.

Well, a tasty carrot like that dangling before his nose was more than even Doctor Boland could seem to ignore. We began to breathe somewhat more easily, and I could almost hear the adding machine in his mind making mental calculations.

"All right, if you guarantee that he's harmless. What seems to be the trouble?"

"I think he has a sticker or something in his ear," Lem explained.

---

disillusionment—*disappointment*
adamant—*stubborn and unwilling to yield*
incinerator—*appliance used to burn trash*

Doctor Boland moved slowly closer, but kept his hands well to himself. "Sort of looks like it, at that. All right, bring him into the hospital. We'll give him some anesthetic and see what we can find."

"Anesthetic?"

"Of course. I wouldn't touch him without putting him to sleep first. We do it most of the time with any animal."

Lem seemed to accept it philosophically. He even held Frisbie, while Doctor Boland applied the saturated cloth over Frisbie's tiny black nose. First the sweat broke out on Lem's forehead; then he got pale. For a minute I thought he was going to faint.

"There it is," Doctor Boland said, laying down a long pair of tweezers which were grasped around a long foxtail-like sticker. "Quite a bit of infection in there, but this penicillin will straighten it up in a hurry. You'd better get your friend a drink of water," he said to me. "You'll find a water cooler down the hallway. Don't get near those dog cages. There are two or three mean ones."

Well, he didn't have to tell me twice. As I went down the middle of the corridor, a couple of big mutts lunged at the wire as though nothing would make them happier than to tear me limb from limb.

Lem was gulping the water when the phone rang. Doctor Boland soon returned. "I have to go pick up a dog down on Elm Street," he said. "You might as well ride over with me. That animal will be some time coming out of the anesthetic. The fresh air will do you good. Especially you, young fellow,"

anesthetic—*medicine that numbs pain*
philosophically—*relying on reason and wisdom*

he indicated Lem, who was still rubbery in the legs. Lem seemed unwilling to leave Frisbie.

"Come on, Lem," I prompted. "He'll be okay."

Doctor Boland changed the cardboard clock in the door window to *Back in 10 Minutes,* and we were soon headed for Elm Street to pick up a fancy mutt that needed a bath.

Having had some difficulty in locating the little Pekingese, which had hidden in a closet at the very mention of a bath, it was somewhat after ten minutes when we returned to the dog-and-cat hospital. On the way back, Doctor Boland had hinted of various and sundry charges for anesthesia (imagine having to gas a skunk!), penicillin, professional services rendered, to say nothing of what he called extraordinary expenses. I could see that he was planning to clear up what-ever mortgages might be hanging over his head. It was going to be a sad time for Lem, on a fifty-cents a week allowance.

We went on in the door. And the minute we stepped inside, I had one of those unexplainable feelings that some-thing was wrong. There seemed to be more noise coming from the animals beyond the office partition. The inner door was ajar.

And suddenly from beyond it came the unmistakable crying of a child. The sound froze us momentarily in our tracks. I say "us," but I think it was Doctor Boland's sudden stiffening, as he dropped the Pekingese to the floor.

"Myra!" he gasped. And I remembered that Myra was his granddaughter. I also knew intuitively that Myra was not allowed in the dog-and-cat hospital.

---

partition—*something that divides a room into sections*
intuitively—*by instinct*

Ordinarily, it might not have been such a startling situation. But the throaty growling of a dog sifted through the many sounds. That growling did not come from the area of heavy wire kennels. One of the dogs was out.

And, from the sound, it was one of the mean ones.

Lem went through the door, with me right at his heels and Doctor Boland crowding close behind.

What we saw was enough to make anyone turn and run. Right in the doorway that led to the kennels stood a large, wild-eyed dog. His teeth were bared. He lunged, then jumped back; he lowered his head and swayed this way and that.

"Grampa! Grampa!" The little girl was crowded back into a corner of the small operating room opposite the doorway to the kennels.

On the floor between her and the doorway which framed the drooling dog stood a small black-and-white furry object. His tiny teeth clicked angrily as he held the large animal at bay.

"Frisbie!" Lem said, but he didn't move to pick up his pet. Frisbie seemed to have things well under control.

Doctor Boland hurried the girl out into the waiting room and closed the door. "Give me that chair," he said, and I could tell that he was having trouble with his voice. The realization of what that dog might have done to his granddaughter was enough to make us all lose our voices.

I slid the chair over to him, and he moved in toward the dog, relieving Frisbie of his vigil.

The dog wasn't mad; he was just mean. But Doctor Boland knew how to handle him.

Then he came back and sat down heavily. The sweat was pouring off his forehead. "We—we've told her a hundred times not to come back here," he explained.

"Kids will be kids," I said.

"There should be padlocks on those kennel doors," Lem said.

"There will be," Doctor Boland said. "There will be!"

Well, there was no sense in anyone bawling out anyone. It was one of those things that could have been very, very

---

at bay—*back at a safe distance*
vigil—*a time of watching*

serious—had it not been for a certain little fellow who wasn't afraid to stand up to anything or anyone.

"It's well that—Frisbie came out of the anesthetic in time," Doctor Boland said. "Son, if that animal ever needs any attention of any kind, bring him to me."

"He could probably use an occasional bath," I put in helpfully, and the Doctor never batted an eye.

Funny thing, too, Lem never did receive a bill from Doctor Boland. And he can't figure out why every once in a while there's a case of cat food left on his doorstep.

"But, Ned," he says, "I didn't order any cat food."

"Frisbie likes it, doesn't he?"

"Likes it? And how!"

"Then stop worrying." I say, "Frisbie ordered it, and he paid for it in full."

Time to Think

1. Why was Ned afraid to get close to Frisbie?
2. What finally convinced Dr. Boland to help Frisbie?
3. What did Frisbie do that proved his worth?

Four Things
Proverbs 30:24–28

There be four things which are little upon the earth,
but they are exceeding wise:

The ants are a people not strong,
yet they prepare their meat in the
summer;

The conies are but a feeble folk, yet
make they their houses in the rocks;

The locusts have no king, yet go
they forth all of them by bands;

The spider taketh hold with her
hands, and is in kings' palaces.

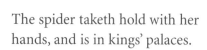

conies—*small, furry animals similar to rabbits*
feeble—*weak*
locust—*a type of grasshopper*

Boots and the Cat

Kitzi Gumensky

Boots was returning from his morning walk. He had made a round of the neighborhood, had looked into several back yards, had played for a few minutes with a couple of dogs, had chased away a crowd of sparrows that had been sitting in the middle of the lawn, had growled in passing at the garbage man, and now felt quite pleased with his morning's work. Boots was a two-year-old wire-haired terrier. He had light brown eyes, a short tail, and a coat which was almost entirely white except for a large black patch that adorned his left ear.

Now, running in the direction of his home, he was thinking with a growing feeling of pleasure of his pail full of last night's soup and bread which was awaiting him on the back porch. After licking it clean, he would go into the living room and stretch himself out on the carpet; or, if no one was around, he might even climb on the couch, and have a little nap. And why not? After all, he was the only pet in the family, except for the green parrot, Mocko, who lived in a cage and did not really count.

Boots was nearing his home, when halfway up the road a cat darted in front of him and began to make her way across the path. Boots gave a cry of joy—the cry of a warrior who sees his enemy given over to his hands—and flew after his prey. The cat had a calm and contented air about her. She

41

was black, with soft white paws, and one of those nice, round heads that you like to see on the shoulders of a cat.

Boots went for her at the rate of forty miles an hour. But the cat did not hurry; she did not seem even to understand that her life was in danger. She trotted quietly on, until Boots was within a yard of her. Then she turned around, sat down in the middle of the road, and looked at Boots with a gently inquiring look.

"I thought I heard somebody trying to catch up with me," she said. "Did you wish to speak to me?"

Boots did not lack pluck. He had chased many a cat up the rainspout and to the roof of the house, and kept her there while he waltzed and barked below, but there was something about the look of this cat that might have chilled the heart of the boldest dog. He stopped abruptly and looked at the cat.

"Can I do anything for you?" repeated the stranger.

By rights at this point Boots ought to have said something. The cat had asked him a plain and simple question. The best he could manage, however, was a faint, soft, whining sound.

pluck—*courage in time of difficulty*

42

"Don't be too shy to ask, if there is something you really want," said the cat, eyeing him with an expression of a lion-tamer.

The first shock over, Boots became himself again.

"Yes, thank you. I mean, no—not at all—very much obliged," he stammered, backing down the road. "I—I am afraid I've made a mistake. I thought I knew you. I hope you will excuse me for disturbing you."

"It is perfectly all right," said the cat, squinting her eyes, "quite a pleasure even. Are you sure that there was nothing you wished to say to me?"

"Not a thing, thank you, not a thing. Perhaps I did before, but now I find I haven't. Awfully sorry about all this—" And Boots backed into a big tree.

"Good morning," said the cat. And getting up, she picked her way daintily and carefully through the tall grass that grew near the fence.

Boots watched the cat from a distance. He saw her jump on a fence and disappear into some back yard. Only after the last sight of her did he get up and begin to trot toward the kitchen door. He felt gloomy. The day, which had started so well and cheerfully, was spoiled by that nuisance of a cat. He was glad that in his house they did not have cat or kitten. Turning a corner, he paused for a second beneath their neighbor's window to investigate a smell. But before he had time to decide whether it was rats or a long-buried bone, the kitchen door of his house swung open, and a voice called, "Here, Boots! Here, Boots!" Boots forgot the smell and slipped through the door into the back porch.

The first thing Boots saw, when coming through the hall into the living room, was the back of a black cat sitting on the mantelpiece. A real living cat! The cat was washing her face.

"A cat in our house!" growled Boots. "She will have to show some speed! I feel like tearing off an ear or two!" And taking a big leap, he rose like a hawk in the direction of the fireplace. The cat turned her head and Boots, catching himself in midair, landed on the floor at the same spot from which he started. He recognized his morning acquaintance.

"Well, well, if this is not our little bashful stranger," said the cat, looking at him with her cold green eyes. Then she turned away and began to wash her paws. Boots felt ashamed. He could not manage to say anything, and to cover his confusion he began to chase a fly.

"Let her think that I was jumping at a fly," he said to himself. "She probably imagines that I am afraid of her."

"I have practically decided to stay," said the cat, having finished her bath.

"Stay where?" stammered Boots.

"Here," said the cat calmly. "I like this house. And the people seem to be quite decent. The milk they gave me was really very good."

"But we don't need any cats," spoke Boots hurriedly. "Perhaps our neighbor needs one. I smelled rats in his basement a few days ago."

"Very kind of you," said the cat, turning her head toward Boots, "but what really made me choose this house was the rug which I noticed in the kitchen. It somehow made me feel that I would be comfortable here. And now, if you'll excuse me, I'll have a little nap. One gets very tired looking for a place to live.

I know you will understand, and will try to be less noisy." And the cat curled up and closed her eyes.

Boots stood for a few minutes in the middle of the room, not knowing what to do. Then he sat down and began to scratch his ear. A cat in his house! A cat that meant to stay and sleep on his rug in the kitchen! This problem required thought, courage, and energy. Boots had these qualities. He knew he had. But how to bring them into action? That was the problem. Again he scratched his ear.

Evening came, and Boots still had no plan. Most of that day he had stayed outside, lying near the kitchen steps with his nose between his paws, thinking very hard; or else he had walked in the yard. He did not go into the house because he did not want to meet the cat before his plans were worked out. She made him feel uncomfortable. He just could not think with her green eyes staring at him. But no idea came.

The sun was already getting low. It hung for a while above the roofs of the houses that stood far away on the hill and then slid behind them. After the sun set, it suddenly became cold. A fresh wind sprang up from the north. Boots wished he were in the warm kitchen on his rug, but he suspected that the place was already occupied by the newcomer. Trembling slightly, he curled up near the kitchen door and tried to sleep. But it was too cold and uncomfortable. So when he saw the cook open the back door, he jumped up and slipped through it into the kitchen. Hardly daring to hope, he looked at his rug near the stove. The cat was not there. She was not even in the kitchen. Boots felt relieved. He went to his rug, stretched himself out on it, and fell into a slumber. The cold wind had chilled him through, and for an hour he shook and whined in his sleep. And then all at once he felt warm and comfortable, as if he were lying on the couch with his back close to the warm cushions.

Boots woke up at dawn. The feeling of something warm and soft behind his back, which came upon him at night, was still there. It was extremely pleasant and comfortable. Boots opened his eyes and turned his head. Curled close to him on the rug slept the cat. Her black head with the pink nose was almost touching his shoulder, and one of the soft white paws rested lightly on his back. For a whole minute Boots stared at the cat; then slowly he put his head down on his paws.

"I may just as well let her stay," he thought, closing his eyes. "She is almost as good as the couch."

In another minute he was sound asleep.

Time to Think

1. Why did Boots become speechless when the cat spoke to him in the road?
2. How did Boots feel when he realized the cat was moving into his house?
3. What do you think made Boots change his attitude toward the cat?

My Cat,
Mrs. Lick-a-Chin

John Ciardi

Some of the cats I know about
Spend a little time in and a lot of time out.
Or a lot of time out and a little time in.
But *my* cat, Mrs. Lick-a-chin,
Never knows *where* she wants to be.
If I let her in she looks at me
And begins to sing that she wants to go out.
So I open the door and she looks about
And begins to sing, "Please let me in!"

Poor silly Mrs. Lick-a-chin!

The thing about cats, as you may find,
Is that no one knows what they have in mind.

And I'll tell you something about that:
No one knows it less than my cat.

How the Rhinoceros Got His Skin

from Just So Stories *by Rudyard Kipling*

We know, of course, how the elephant got his long trunk, how the camel got his hump, and how the rhinoceros got his baggy skin—God made them that way. It is fun, though, to read the humorous explanations Rudyard Kipling gives in his famous book, *Just So Stories.*

Once upon a time, on an uninhabited island on the shores of the Red Sea, there lived a Parsee with nothing but his hat and his knife and a cooking-stove of the kind that you must particularly never touch. And one day he took flour and water and currants and plums and sugar and things, and made himself one cake which was two feet across and three feet thick. He put it on the stove because *he* was allowed to cook on that stove, and he baked it and he baked it till it was all done brown and smelt most sentimental. But just as he was going to eat it there came down to the beach from the Altogether Uninhabited Interior one Rhinoceros with a horn on his nose, two piggy eyes, and few manners. In those days the Rhinoceros's skin fitted him quite tight. There were no wrinkles in it anywhere. He looked exactly like a Noah's Ark Rhinoceros, but much bigger. All the same, he had no manners then, and he has no manners now, and he never will have any manners. He said, "How!" and the Parsee left that cake and climbed to the top of a palm tree. And the rhinoceros upset the oil-stove with his nose, and the cake rolled on the sand, and he spiked that cake on the horn of his nose, and

currants—*dried berries, much like raisins*

he ate it, and he went away, waving his tail, to the desolate and Exclusively Uninhabited Interior. Then the Parsee came down from his palm tree and put the stove on its legs and recited the following *Sloka,* which, as you have not heard, I will now proceed to relate:—

Them that take cakes
Which the Parsee-man bakes
Makes dreadful mistakes.

And there was a great deal more in that than you would think.

desolate—*deserted*
Sloka (slō′kə)

49

Because, five weeks later, there was a heat wave in the Red Sea, and the Parsee took off his hat; but the Rhinoceros took off his skin and carried it over his shoulder as he came down to the beach to bathe. In those days it buttoned underneath with three buttons and looked like a waterproof. He said nothing whatever about the Parsee's cake, because he had eaten it all; and he never had any manners, then, since, or henceforward. He waddled straight into the water and blew bubbles through his nose, leaving his skin on the beach.

Presently the Parsee came by and found the skin, and he smiled one smile that ran all round his face two times. Then he danced three times round the skin and rubbed his hands. Then he went to his camp and filled his hat with cake crumbs, for the Parsee never ate anything but cake, and never swept out his camp. He took that skin, he shook that skin, and he scrubbed that skin, and he rubbed that skin just as full of old, dry, stale, tickly cake crumbs and some burned currants as ever it could *possibly* hold. Then he climbed to the top of his palm tree and waited for the Rhinoceros to come out of the water and put it on.

And the Rhinoceros did. He buttoned it up with the three buttons, and it tickled like cake crumbs in bed. Then he wanted to scratch, but that made it worse; and then he lay down on the sands and rolled and rolled and rolled, and every time he rolled the cake crumbs tickled him worse and worse and worse. Then he ran to the palm tree and rubbed and rubbed and rubbed himself against it.

He rubbed so much and so hard that he rubbed his skin into a great fold over his shoulders, and another fold underneath, where the buttons used to be (but he rubbed the buttons off), and he rubbed some more folds over his legs. And it spoiled his temper, but it didn't make the least difference to the cake crumbs. They were inside his skin and they tickled. So he went home, very angry indeed and horribly scratchy; and from that day to this every rhinoceros has great folds in his skin on account of the cake crumbs inside.

But the Parsee came down from his palm tree, wearing his hat, from which the rays of the sun were reflected in splendor, packed up his cooking-stove, and went away in the direction of the Marshes of Sonaput.

Sonaput (sŏn′ə·p͞ot′)

Time to Think

1. What did the Rhinoceros do that made the Parsee angry?
2. What made the Rhinoceros take off his skin and go into the water?
3. What did the Parsee do to punish the Rhinoceros?
4. How do we know that this story is purely fictional?

The Fox and the Grapes

Joseph Lauren

One summer's day a fox was passing through
A vineyard; faint he was and hungry, too.
When suddenly his keen eye chanced to fall
Upon a bunch of grapes above the wall.
"Ha! Just the thing!" he said. "Who could resist it?"
He eyed the purple cluster—jumped—and missed it.
"Ahem!" he coughed. "I'll take more careful aim,"
And sprang again. Results were much the same,
Although his leaps were desperate and high.
At length he paused to wipe a tearful eye,
And shrug a shoulder. "I am not so dry,
And lunch is bound to come within the hour . . .
Besides," he said, "I'm sure those grapes are sour."

The moral is: We seem to want the peach
That always dangles just beyond our reach.
Yet, like the fox, we must not be upset
When sometimes things are just too hard to get.

Famous Dogs
Author Unknown

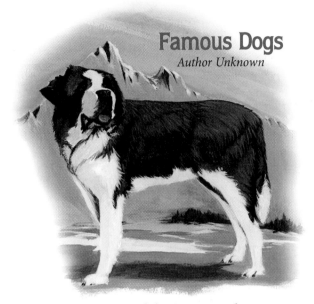

My name is Barry, of the St. Bernard;
When the snows drift deep and the wind blows hard,
You may hear my bark, and see me flying
To guide the lost and rescue the dying.
Although I wear no collar of gold,
All over the world my praise is told.

The Spaniel am I,—in Spain I was found;
but in every land I have been renowned.
I am always faithful, docile, and wise;
I have silken hair and beautiful eyes;
Should you treat me well or treat me ill,
As long as I live I'll love you still.

docile—*easily taught*

I am the Newfoundland, trusty and bold;
I love the water, and do as I'm told.
I'm sometimes rough in my bounding play,—
Please to excuse it, 'tis only my way,—
And many a life I've been known to save
From the cruel depth of the pitiless wave.

I am the Greyhound, so slim, you know;
I came from Asia long, long ago.
In Turkey, I'm called the "dog of the street";
In Russia, I the wolf can beat;
In Italy, I am a lady's pet:
All over the world my race is met.

I am the Mastiff, a watchdog true;
Many a noble deed I do;
To guard your homes I take delight;
My bay sounds far through the silent night.
I've fought the lion, and conquered the bear;
My friends I protect; let my foes beware.

54

I am the dog of the Eskimo;
I drag their sleds over the snow;
I can run and leap; I laugh at the cold;
I'm useful, hardy, strong, and bold.
In an icebound hut with my master I dwell;
I toil for him, and he loves me well.

Time to Think

1. Which two dogs are able to travel through snow?
2. Which dog do you think would make the best house pet?
3. Name interesting characteristics about each dog.

Hold on to America

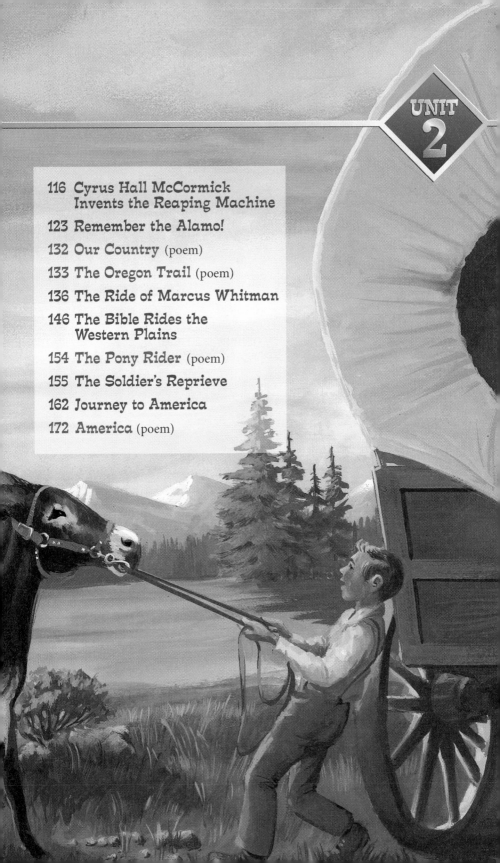

Hold on to America

JoAnn M. Stiff

When Columbus discovered America,
He did not know that he had found
A land to be populated with free men,
Where peace and justice would abound.
A seed of truth was planted in the new land
That Columbus could not have known
Would be cultivated and nurtured in love
After it was carefully sown.

Men like Washington, Jefferson, and Lincoln
Helped the seedling grow straight and tall.
And patriotic men have given their lives
So our nation would never fall.

May we always cherish this precious freedom,
Keep it tightly within our clasp.
There is no other government in the world
With such liberty in its grasp.
But to remain free we must do our duty,
Stand firm and staunch and pray;
God has given us a country richly blessed . . .
Let us help to keep it that way.

---

cultivated—*prepared for growth*
staunch—*not moving*

The Mayflower Compact

A Play in One Act by Eleanore Hubbard

Before the Pilgrims left England to cross the Atlantic, they
secured from King James a patent, or document, giving them
permission to settle in the part of the New World ruled by
England. The winds took the *Mayflower* far north of her
destination, but the Pilgrims decided to end their difficult
voyage and settle at Plymouth. Knowing that orderly life
would be impossible without the protection and discipline of
governmental authority, these God-fearing men determined to
establish their own government. This they did with the
written agreement we call the Mayflower Compact.

Time:
November 21, 1620

Scene:
Cabin of the Mayflower
in Provincetown Harbor, Cape Cod.

Characters:

John Carver	*John Allerton*
William Bradford	*Roger Wilder*
Edward Winslow	*William Trevor*
William Brewster	*Ely,* a Seaman
Miles Standish	*Other Pilgrims*

JOHN CARVER: You well know, my friends, how our good ship *Mayflower* has been tossed about on the ocean like a cork and driven hundreds of miles from its course.

JOHN ALLERTON: Save for that goodly iron screw with which I did mend the cracked timber, she would have foundered.

JOHN CARVER: But by the providence of God we have made harbor, and I now propose that Captain Miles Standish and a chosen party of men go spy out the land.

ROGER WILDER: What! On this wild New England shore! The land owned by the London Company that sent us is far to the south!

---

propose—*to give an idea*

JOHN CARVER: Verily. But the elements and the grace of God hath led us here. We are all weary of the sea, and it seems fitting that we should find settlement on this Cape Cod.

ROGER WILDER: But the patent! It calls not for Cape Cod!

WILLIAM TREVOR *(softly to Wilder)*: Sh! Protest not. If they do make settlement here, the patent is not binding, and they cannot hold us to the laws of the company.

ROGER WILDER: That is so. We can be free to do as we so wish.

ELY: Not having a patent, they will have no laws, say you? Hah! No laws; then we can do as we will.

WILLIAM BREWSTER *(overhearing)*: Not so! Not so! Wilder, Trevor, and Ely! John Carver, these hired men do threaten lawlessness.

ROGER WILDER *(sullenly)*: If you do not abide by the patent, you cannot hold us.

JOHN CARVER *(sternly)*: Stay, Roger Wilder! Talk not in that ungodly fashion. We be a God-fearing body, law-abiding, and self-respecting. We hold not with such willful sayings.

WILLIAM TREVOR: But if there is no authority to make or enforce laws, what doth prevent us doing as we please?

WILLIAM BRADFORD: We, this Pilgrim company, will prevent such misrule. What say you, John Carver, William Brewster, and the rest, to our drawing up a contract to

---

elements—*weather*
patent—*an official document that states the rights of an owner*

take the place of the patent, whereunto we can put our signatures to make it solemn and binding.

ALL *(except Wilder, Trevor, and Ely)*: Aye! Aye!

EDWARD WINSLOW: In it we can declare the purpose for which we come to these new shores and our decision to make and enforce such laws as will be necessary for the good of the colony.

JOHN CARVER: And those who sign shall, for themselves and for their families, thereby promise to submit to and obey the laws that shall be so made and so ordered.

ALL: Aye! Aye!

WILLIAM BREWSTER *(who has been writing during the discussion)*: What say you to this? *(Reads.)*

> In the name of God, Amen. We whose names are underwritten, the loyal subjects of our dread sovereign Lord, King James, by the grace of God, of Great Britain, France, and Ireland king, defender of the faith, etc. Having undertaken, for the glory of God, and advancement of the Christian faith, and honour of our king and country, a voyage to plant the first colony in the Northern parts of Virginia, do by these presents solemnly and mutually in the presence of God, and one of another, covenant and combine ourselves together into a civil body politic, for our better ordering and preservation and furtherance of the ends aforesaid; and by virture hereof to enact, constitute, and frame such just and equal laws, ordinances, acts,

---

mutually—*in agreement with each other*
politic—*having to do with civil government*
ordinances—*regulations set by the government*

constitutions, and offices, from time to time, as shall be thought most meet and convenient for the general good of the colony, unto which we promise all due submission and obedience.

JOHN CARVER: Aye!

WILLIAM BRADFORD: Good!

EDWARD WINSLOW: 'Tis excellent!

JOHN ALLERTON: Most fitting!

WILLIAM BRADFORD: That doth set forth our cause most clearly and in right proper language.

JOHN CARVER: And by its acceptance we should bind ourselves in a righteous civic body to make our own laws and to obey them.

WILLIAM BRADFORD: Aye, it will be as firm as any patent, and in some respects more sure.

JOHN CARVER: All those, therefore, who do approve this compact signify by saying "Aye."

ALL *(except rebellious three)*: Aye! Aye!

JOHN CARVER: Those opposed say "Nay."

(The three look sullen, but no one speaks.)

WILLIAM BREWSTER: 'Tis agreed. Then shall we sign?

ALL: Aye!

JOHN CARVER: The heads of families shall sign as representatives of their wives and children.

ALL: Yea, verily.

JOHN CARVER: So! *(Writing.)* John—Carver. *(Hands pen to Bradford.)*

WILLIAM BRADFORD: William—Bradford. *(Pen passes to Winslow, Brewster, Standish, etc. While others are signing, Bradford makes proposal.)* I now propose that we choose Mr. John Carver our governor for this year.

EDWARD WINSLOW: Yea! He is a man godly and well-approved amongst us.

ALL: Aye! Aye! Governor John Carver! We confirm John Carver as governor.

JOHN CARVER: Then with the help of God I shall endeavor to serve the office with justice and righteousness. And may God ever guide our Pilgrim band in His way and truth.

ALL: Amen!

Righteousness exalteth a nation:
but sin is a reproach to any people.
—Proverbs 13:34

Time to Think

1. Did the Pilgrims land where they had intended? Where did they land?
2. Why did William Brewster suggest that they write a contract?
3. By signing the contract, what did the Pilgrims promise to do?
4. Did every person sign the contract?
5. Why was John Carver chosen as governor?
6. How did the Pilgrims view authority?

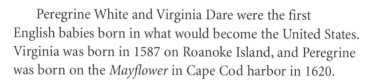

Peregrine White
and Virginia Dare

Rosemary and Stephen Vincent Benét

Peregrine White and Virginia Dare were the first
English babies born in what would become the United States.
Virginia was born in 1587 on Roanoke Island, and Peregrine
was born on the *Mayflower* in Cape Cod harbor in 1620.

Peregrine White
And Virginia Dare
Were the first real Americans
Anywhere.

Others might find it
Strange to come
Over the ocean
To make a home,

England and memory
Left behind—
But Virginia and Peregrine
Didn't mind.

One of them born
On Roanoke
And the other cradled
In Pilgrim oak.

Rogues might bicker
And good men pray.
Did they pay attention?
No, not they.

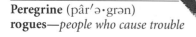

Peregrine (pâr′ə·grən)
rogues—*people who cause trouble*

66

Men might grumble
And women weep
But Virginia and Peregrine
Went to sleep.

They had their dinner
And napped and then
When they woke up
It was dinner again.

They didn't worry,
They didn't wish,
They didn't farm
And they didn't fish.

There was lots of work
But they didn't do it.
They were pioneers
But they never knew it.

Wolves in the forest
And Indian drums!
Virginia and Peregrine
Sucked their thumbs.

They were only babies.
They didn't care.
Peregrine White
And Virginia Dare.

A Poem to King George

Kathryn Kilby Borland
and Helen Ross Speicher

When the little African girl was only seven or eight years old, she was brought to Colonial America and sold to Mr. and Mrs. John Wheatley as a slave. The Wheatleys named her Phillis, and she became like a daughter to them. Viewing Phillis as a member of the family rather than a servant, the Wheatleys' children Mary and Nathaniel taught her to read and write. After being with the Wheatleys only a short time, Phillis discovered that her education had sparked a special God-given talent.

Phillis sat up in bed. It wasn't daylight. Some sound must have awakened her, but the night was quiet again. She lay back and closed her eyes, wondering whether she was mistaken. Then she heard a bell ringing, again and again, louder and louder.

68

She ran to open her window and leaned out into the warm May darkness. Far down the street she could hear a horse's hoofbeats. Then a man on horseback came galloping down the street. He was shouting, but Phillis could not understand what he said.

Now she could hear Mr. Wheatley's window being thrown up with an angry sound. "What's all this?" he called out crossly.

"Good news! Good news!" the horseman shouted, but he didn't slow down.

Phillis noticed lighted windows in other houses up and down the street. One or two men had come out on the front steps with dressing gowns over their nightshirts.

"What is it?" they called to one another, but nobody seemed to know.

Before long a group of young men came running down the street with lighted torches. They were throwing their hats in the air.

"Three cheers for King George! Three cheers for the Sons of Liberty!" they shouted. Finally Mr. Wheatley got the attention of one of the young men.

"We got good news about the Stamp Act, sir," the man called. "Word just came that the Stamp Act has been repealed!"

Phillis could hear Nat's shout from his room. "We did it! We did it!"

No one in the Wheatley household, or probably in all of Boston, went back to sleep that night. The bells went on

---

repealed—*taken away*

ringing. Soon drums were beating steadily, and once in a while the boom of a cannon could be heard.

Breakfast next morning was a happy meal. Everyone was hungry after the excitement of the night. Sukey, the kitchen servant, beamed as she brought in huge platters of codfish cakes and corn bread.

"Well," Mrs. Wheatley said, "from now on Boston should be the way it used to be. No more riots. No more Sons of Liberty."

"Oh, I think we'll still have Sons of Liberty, Mother," Nat said. "We want to be sure England doesn't try anything else."

"Don't speak of England as if it were a foreign country, Nat," his father said. "We shall always be English."

"Of course we will, Father, no matter where we live. But we want to be treated like all other Englishmen."

The clock in the hall struck eight, and still Mr. Wheatley sat at the table with his family. "Aren't you going to the tailor shop today, John?" Mrs. Wheatley asked.

"Precious little trade I would have today," Mr. Wheatley replied. "This will be a holiday in all of Boston."

"Can Nat take Phillis and me out to see the excitement?" Mary asked.

"Certainly he can, unless he has other plans," Mr. Wheatley answered.

"No, not really," Nat answered slowly. Phillis was sure Nat would rather have gone by himself, but he seldom could bring himself to hurt anyone's feelings.

---

riots—*angry displays by large crowds*

By the time Mary and Phillis were ready, crowds of people were filling the narrow streets. Most of them were dressed in their best Sunday clothes. Flags were waving from many of the houses, and everybody was laughing.

As Nat, Mary, and Phillis turned toward the Boston Commons, Phillis said, "Oh, look at the Liberty Tree. Isn't it exciting?" The enormous elm tree had been named the Liberty Tree because it was one of the favorite meeting places of the Sons of Liberty. Now flags and colored streamers of every color hung from its branches. They looked as if they had grown there, but of course some people had worked hard to put them there during the night.

The celebration lasted all day. Bands wandered through the crowds, playing loudly if not well. The bells kept ringing.

That night there was a fireworks display on the Commons. There had never been such fireworks in Boston. The air was filled with rockets, bright serpents, and spinning pinwheels. At eleven o'clock twenty-one rockets and sixteen dozen serpents were sent up all at once for a glorious finish.

A loud cheer went up for King George. Phillis wished that King George could know how happy the people were about what had been done. She wished someone would tell him.

After Phillis went to bed that night she tossed and turned. Some idea was trying to form in her brain, but she was too tired to think about it. In the middle of the night the idea suddenly came to her.

She would write King George about how the colonists felt. Perhaps she would even write it in verse. She had written a poem not long before, but had not shown it to anyone.

She crept quietly out of bed and her candle burned for
hours while she wrote. When she woke up in the morning
she looked at what she had written. What a ridiculous idea,
she thought. How could I ever have imagined that the king
would read anything written by a young servant girl? She
left the poem on the little table by her bed and almost
forgot it.

A few weeks later Phillis was sick in bed with a cold.
One morning Mrs. Wheatley brought a bowl of porridge for
her breakfast. As she set the bowl on the little table, she
noticed a scrap of paper there. She picked up the paper and
asked, "What is this, Phillis?"

Phillis was embarrassed. "Oh it's nothing, Mrs. Wheatley, nothing at all."

"But it is, Phillis. These are beautiful words. Did you copy this poem from a book?"

"Oh, no, Mrs. Wheatley. I wrote it myself, but it isn't very good."

"You wrote it yourself? Phillis, this is remarkable. Why didn't you show it to us?"

"I was ashamed to show it to you, Mrs. Wheatley. I actually wrote it to send to the king, and then I decided that would be silly. Besides the poem isn't any good."

"May I show it to Mr. Wheatley?"

Phillis hesitated. Probably Mr. Wheatley would think the poem was foolish. But she said, "Yes, of course," and Mrs. Wheatley did not seem to notice her lack of enthusiasm.

That evening after supper the whole family came up to her room. Mr. Wheatley was holding the poem in his hand. He looked very solemn, and Phillis feared he was angry. Then he cleared his throat and said, "Mrs. Wheatley tells me you wrote this poem."

"Yes, sir," Phillis answered feebly.

"Now are you sure you really wrote it yourself? Sometimes we read something and don't remember it. Later we remember it but don't remember where we saw it. Then we may think we thought of it ourselves. Do you see what I mean, Phillis?"

"Yes, sir, I do," Phillis said, "But that isn't the way it was this time. I wanted somehow to make King George see how grateful we were. This was the only way I could think of. I know it was foolish of me, sir. I guess I was just excited over the celebration."

"I told you, Father," Mary said. "Phillis reads and reads and reads. She uses words I don't even know how to use."

Mr. Wheatley cleared his throat again. "Well, then," he said, "in that case it's remarkable. Have you written any other poems?"

"Yes, sir. I wrote one about Harvard College. Would you like to see it?"

A few minutes later Mr. Wheatley left the room with both poems in his hand. Then one evening several days later he told Phillis that she was to go to the State House with him the next morning. "A few gentlemen there would like to ask you about your poems."

"They'll be angry," Phillis thought. "Mr. Wheatley shouldn't have told them."

Usually Phillis enjoyed looking at the gilded lion and unicorn over the State House door. Today she was too frightened even to look at them. Mr. Wheatley had told her that the most important men in Boston would talk with her.

Mr. Wheatley led her into the Council Chamber. Several stern-looking men who were seated at a long table looked up at her. Others looked down from gold frames on the wall.

"Stand at this end of the table where we can see you," one of the men said. He was holding her poems in his hand.

"Yes, sir," Phillis said in a low voice. She folded her cold hands in front of her to stop them from shaking.

---

gilded—*trimmed in gold*
unicorn—*a fictional animal usually pictured as a*
   horse with one horn in the center of its head

"Mr. Wheatley tells us you wrote these poems," said one of the men.

"Yes, sir."

"Did anyone give you any help?"

"No, sir."

"Why did you write about Harvard College?"

"Because, sir, Mr. Nat brought back so much from there for Miss Mary and me to study and talk about. He even taught Latin to Miss Mary, and she taught it to me."

"Latin, eh?" a man said with interest. "Can you tell me what *E pluribus unum* means?"

Phillis smiled. "Yes, sir. It means 'one from many,'" she said.

Some of the other gentlemen asked questions in Latin which she was able to answer. They also asked her what books she liked to read. Then they began asking about her poems.

"Tell us what you meant by these lines, 'May every clime with equal gladness see A monarch's smile can set his subjects free'."

The speaker was Mr. Samuel Adams. Phillis had often seen him at the Wheatleys' house. "I meant that we were glad the king used his power to make us happy. I'm sorry the meaning wasn't clear, sir," she said.

"I think it was quite clear."

E pluribus unum (ē plōōr'ĭ·bŭs ū'nŭm)
clime—*climate*
monarch—*a king or queen*
subjects—*people under a ruler's authority*

The other gentlemen nodded. They asked her questions almost all morning. She was so tired before they were through that she hardly knew what she answered.

At the end of the questioning, Mr. Adams smiled and said, "We shall send your poem to the king, and we hope that you will write many more. You have a great gift, young woman, a very great gift, and it must be used."

Phillis Wheatley did use her great gift to become the first black woman writer in America. Though her life was brief, only about thirty years, Phillis Wheatley used her talent to please people and glorify God.

Time to Think

1. What made Phillis write the poem to King George?
2. Why did Mr. and Mrs. Wheatley think Phillis had copied the poem?
3. How did the men at the State House test Phillis's knowledge?
4. What do you think impressed the men at the State House most about Phillis?

Scout for George Washington

Ivy Bolton

"Tory! Tory! Down with the Tory!" the boys yelled.

Crowded against the wall, Tony looked helplessly at the angry boys about him. He was no match for Will Street and his friends. But as they fell upon him, Tony Bradford fought back as hard as he could, trying gamely to defend himself.

gamely—*without yielding*

It was the afternoon before Christmas and, for December, an unusually warm day. The ice on the frozen Delaware River was beginning to soften. Tony's feet slipped in the melting snow and mud of the road.

Suddenly the boys pressed forward, all attacking Tony at once and shoving him away from the wall. Tony could feel himself falling. Just then, a strong hand pulled the attackers away.

The rescuer was a tall man in a shabby blue and tan uniform, with a dark cloak hanging from his shoulders. The boys' eyes widened as the man pulled Tony up, for George Washington was a well-known figure.

"Cowards!" cried General Washington scornfully.

"Tony is a Tory traitor!" replied the boys stoutly. "He's a traitor—just like his father. They cross the river to serve the enemy. We don't want his likes around."

The general answered sternly. "Four to one is a coward's fight. You are all taller and stronger than this lad. Get you gone and leave him alone."

They went. Tony looked up at his protector. Kindly eyes smiled down into his. The boy rubbed a sleeve across his face.

"Hurt, lad?"

"Nothing to matter," Tony gulped. But to his dismay, the lump in his throat grew bigger, and tears began to stream down his face. "If only it were not true that my father is a traitor," he sobbed remorsefully.

The general threw his arm across Tony's shoulders. "Your father is Jacob Bradford, the butcher and farmer?" he asked.

Tony nodded.

"And you believe in freedom for America, but you have to serve the Hessians?"

"Yes—oh, I hate it all!" Tony burst out. "For a while I lived with my mother's people, and they speak the language of the Hessians. So Father makes me go with him because I understand the Hessians better than he can. I wanted to come to you and fight for freedom, only Father . . ."

"Your father would not let you go, of course. You will need a little more height and weight first," the general said with a smile. "Perhaps you are helping more than you know, my lad, for every brave and loyal heart helps.

"Your first duty is to your father. Stick by him. Do not be quick to judge. Let us walk a bit."

It was not of battles, of victory, or of defeat, that the general talked as they walked by the frozen Delaware River. It was of unknown heroes—men and boys who worked alone at tasks that brought no glory.

The walk ended at the Continentals' camp. And what a pitiful camp it was! A smoky fire here and there gave a little warmth. In front of their tumbledown huts, shabby soldiers hobbled about with nothing but rags on their half-frozen feet.

It was a miserable place, and one that had been in frequent danger. The Hessians had planned to attack it again and again—Tony himself had heard them talking about it—but always their plans went amiss.

Suddenly there was a shout, and two men came into the camp dragging a prisoner. Tony gave a gasp of terror. The prisoner was his own father!

Hessians (hĕsh′ənz)—*German soldiers*
amiss—*not as planned*

80

The soldiers saluted their general. "We have caught the
Tory spy red-handed," they announced triumphantly. "He
was loading his cart with meat for the Hessians at Trenton.
Shall we hang him at once?"

"We are Americans," General Washington replied sternly.
"Americans do not hang people without a fair trial. Besides,
Christmas Eve is no time for a trial or a hanging. Release this

man." Then, nodding at Tony's father, he added, "Come here. I want to question you."

Reluctantly the soldiers let their prisoner loose and moved away grumbling.

General Washington walked over to Jacob Bradford. Tony stood there trembling.

But as he watched the two men, Tony grew more and more puzzled. The general did not seem angry, and his father was not afraid. They talked a few minutes, and then Jacob Bradford hurried out of the gate.

General Washington turned to Tony. "Come with me, boy," he said.

He took Tony into his own hut and spoke soothingly to him while he washed the mud from the boy's face. Then, as Tony stammered his thanks, the general said, "Now go after your father, boy."

Tony ran off. His father was waiting for him beside a cart filled with meat and sacks of flour and winter vegetables.

Surely his father would not go over to Trenton now, Tony thought. It was getting late, and the sun was already setting.

"You will have to help me," his father said in his quiet way. "I'll need a hand over at Trenton, belike. Get up."

He climbed to the driver's seat, and Tony scrambled up beside him with a heavy heart. "Stick by your father and do not judge," General Washington had said. Well, he would obey the general's orders, hard though it was.

As they crossed the bridge, Tony noticed that there were big dark cracks in the ice.

---

belike—*probably*

When they reached the other side, Hessian soldiers ran up to meet them. They were warmly dressed in their green furred cloaks, with furred gloves on their hands.

The soldiers shouted with delight when they examined the heavily loaded cart.

"A holiday, a holiday!" all of them shouted. "No guards needed on Christmas Eve!"

"Did they say *no guards?*" Jacob Bradford asked his son in a whisper.

"No guards," Tony whispered, puzzled by the question. Why should his father care?

Jacob Bradford spoke in a loud voice. "These men will ride on into Trenton with me. You may go back, Tony."

Then he dropped his voice so that Tony could scarcely hear him. "Go to the general and tell him that the Hessians are keeping Christmas. Tell him what you just heard." He gave Tony a little push. "Hurry, and may God go with you."

Tony's heart was thumping wildly as he jumped down from the cart and hurried back toward the bridge.

It was completely dark now. He moved as fast as he could.

He was halfway across the bridge when he heard voices in front of him. "I tell you, it was Tony on that cart," Will Street was insisting. "We will catch him here and beat him up, the good-for-nothing traitor!" Then he added jeeringly, "There will be no General Washington here to help him this time!"

Tony stood still, wondering what to do. The message! How could he get the message to the general? There was only one other way—the river.

He shook with fear as he remembered the threatening cracks in the ice. It was melting so fast that a break might come any minute, without warning. He would surely die if he were plunged into those icy waters. But the message *must* be delivered to General Washington.

Tony pressed his chattering teeth together and climbed over the railing, down to the ice. Then he set out to cross the wide stream. Slipping, sliding, lurching over the uneven ice, recovering his balance with a despairing gasp, he continued his terrifying crossing.

At last he climbed up the bank. He was almost too tired to stand, but he forced himself to run. The boys might still try to stop him.

There was a roar like thunder up the river. The ice was breaking! In fifteen minutes the river would be a mass of jagged blocks of ice.

He stumbled into the camp. The guard stared at him, but took him at once to the general. General Washington's tired and discouraged face lighted up as he listened to the message.

"Our chance!" he cried, and ordered the call to arms to be sounded instantly.

"We'll use the boats," he announced. "The Hessians will never expect us to dare such a project through the broken ice."

General Washington entered the first boat. "Come along, Tony," he said. "But mind you keep out of the fight."

The general stood in the bow, pushing away jagged blocks of ice with a great pole.

---

lurching—*moving forward uncertainly*
call to arms—*announcement to prepare to fight*

"Keep out of the fight, lad," he reminded Tony again as they landed.

But there was no fighting. The surprise was complete. By dawn, Trenton was in the hands of General Washington's army.

The church bells rang out for Christmas and for the first victory of the Continental army in many weary months.

In the evening there was a feast for the victors at Trenton, from the plentiful stores laid up there. When all were seated at the feast, one of the officers sprang to his feet. "A toast to our great commander!" he cried. "A toast to the man who has led us and saved us—a toast to General Washington!"

A storm of cheers answered him. General Washington bowed and smiled. Then he held up his hand for silence.

"Not to me are the chief thanks due," he said quietly. "We have passed through many bad months. We have been in great danger again and again, but we have been saved.

"Not by miracle or magic have we been saved, but by the help of two people. Jacob Bradford brought his produce here to Trenton and mixed with the Hessians. He knew very little of their language. Tony, his lad, knew more.

"Bradford brought his warnings to me in spite of threats from his own people, who did not know he was working for me. Tonight his lad crossed the icy river, full of cracks, knowing that the break might come any moment." He smiled at Tony.

"This boy, Tony, loved his country enough, and was daring enough, to risk that terrible crossing. He brought me the message which has enabled us to achieve this victory tonight."

General George Washington stood tall and straight. "A toast, officers and men, to two heroes—a toast to Jacob Bradford and to Tony, his son!"

Time to Think

1. Why did Will Street and his friends want to attack Tony?
2. Who saved Tony from the boys?
3. Did Tony think his father was a traitor?
4. Why did Tony's father take him when he visited the Hessians?
5. What order did General Washington give Tony?
6. Why weren't the Hessians prepared when General Washington's army attacked?
7. To whom did Washington give credit for the victory?
8. What good character traits did Tony and his father show?

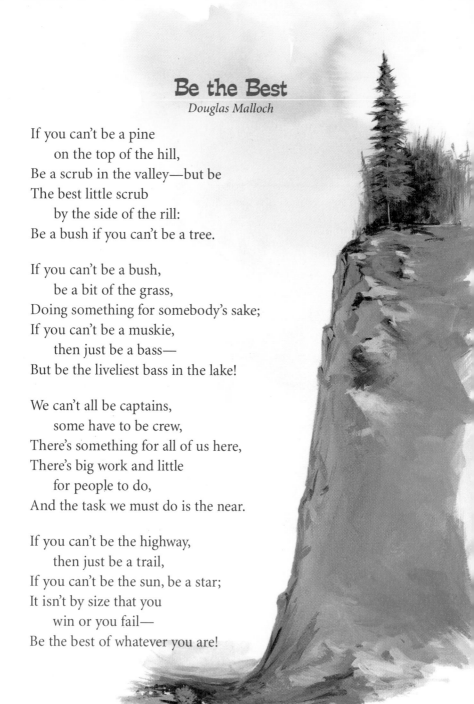

Be the Best

Douglas Malloch

If you can't be a pine
    on the top of the hill,
Be a scrub in the valley—but be
The best little scrub
    by the side of the rill:
Be a bush if you can't be a tree.

If you can't be a bush,
    be a bit of the grass,
Doing something for somebody's sake;
If you can't be a muskie,
    then just be a bass—
But be the liveliest bass in the lake!

We can't all be captains,
    some have to be crew,
There's something for all of us here,
There's big work and little
    for people to do,
And the task we must do is the near.

If you can't be the highway,
    then just be a trail,
If you can't be the sun, be a star;
It isn't by size that you
    win or you fail—
Be the best of whatever you are!

scrub—*a short bush*
rill—*a small stream*
muskie—*a large fish caught for food*

"The Spirit of '76"

James Cross Giblin

On the Fourth of July, patriotic paintings and drawings are often published on the front pages of newspapers. The painting that probably appears more frequently than any other is called *The Spirit of '76*.

There are three figures in the painting, all of them playing musical instruments. A white-haired old man beats a drum, a middle-aged man with a bandaged head plays a fife, and a young drummer boy looks admiringly at the old drummer. Behind them marches a company of Revolutionary soldiers. One of the soldiers is carrying the first American flag.

Archibald Willard, the man who painted *The Spirit of '76*, lived in the small town of Wellington, Ohio, and worked in a carriage factory. In his spare time he painted landscapes and humorous pictures. On July 4, 1871, he got the idea for the painting that was to bring him worldwide fame.

---

fife—*a small flute*
landscapes—*paintings of scenery*

Early that morning, Willard saw three boys—two drummers and a fife player—getting ready to march in the Wellington holiday parade. One drummer was juggling his sticks, and all three were good-humoredly bumping into one another. Willard made a quick pencil sketch of the boys, and meant to do a painting of them later.

A friend who saw the sketch gave Willard a different idea. Instead of a comic scene, the friend suggested that Willard paint a serious picture with a patriotic theme. The artist was intrigued. It would be unlike anything he had ever done.

As he planned the painting, Willard remembered stories told him by his grandfather, who had fought in the Revolutionary War. They helped him decide what figures to include. Willard's own father posed as the old drummer, and a Civil War comrade of Willard's posed as the fife player. Henry Devereaux, the thirteen-year-old son of a railroad president, was the model for the drummer boy.

The large painting, eight by ten feet, was completed early in 1876. That year marked the centennial of the Declaration of Independence. Willard heard there would be an exhibit of paintings at the grand Centennial Exhibition in Philadelphia. He decided to submit *The Spirit of '76*.

The Centennial Commission had said that only classical paintings from the major art centers of Europe and America would be eligible for the exhibit. But when the Commission members saw Willard's painting, they were so moved that they accepted it at once. *The Spirit of '76* quickly became

---

intrigued—*interested*
Devereaux (dĕv′ə·rōōks′)
exhibit—*a display*

submit—*to present as an option*
eligible—*qualified*

one of the most popular pictures in the entire exhibit. It attracted such large crowds that special guards were assigned to protect it.

After the Centennial Exhibition closed, General Devereaux, the father of the model for the drummer boy, bought the painting from Archibald Willard. Then he sent it on a long tour of the country. It finally came to rest in Marblehead, Massachusetts, General Devereaux's birthplace. There it can be seen today.

Over the past one hundred years, *The Spirit of '76* has been reproduced on china plates, towels and napkins, as well as on posters and greeting cards. It has come to symbolize the courage of Revolutionary War soldiers, who were willing to fight for America's right to govern itself. And it reminds people everywhere of why we celebrate Independence Day.

Time to Think

1. What was Mr. Willard's original idea for a painting?
2. Describe what Mr. Willard actually painted.
3. Whose stories of the Revolutionary War helped Mr. Willard with his painting?
4. Why do you think *The Spirit of '76* is such a popular painting?

Song of Our Land

Annette Wynne

Mountainland, fountainland, shoreland, and sea,
God's land thou art surely—His gift to the free;
How blest are thy children wherever they roam
To claim thee their country, their hope, and their home.

I love thee, my country, O great be thy fame;
I love thy dear banner—I honor thy name;
I'll live for thee, die for thee, serve no land but thee:
My country forever, great land of the free!

Strength in Union

Charlie Johnson

"Dan, quick, wake up! You won't believe what is outside!"

Dan Webster was fast asleep on the straw bed. It had been raining steadily for the past two days, and now the pitter-patter of the raindrops on the tin roof settled softly in Dan's ears, making it difficult for him to arise. But his older brother, Zeke, continued to call excitedly from the window. After a moment, Dan leaped out of bed.

"I'm coming, Zeke," Dan promised as he hastily pulled on his clothes. Excitement began to swell in Dan also. "What is it, Zeke?" he asked as he ran to the window.

The two brothers gazed in disbelief at the sight which lay in front of them: the field was almost completely under water. Dan was amazed at how the river had risen with only two days of rain. How the width of the river had grown! The water was lapping about fifty yards from the Webster house. The possibility of evacuation entered the boys' minds; it sobered Zeke but excited young Dan. The brothers hurried outside.

Zeke's scanning survey of the vast area suddenly stopped. Dan could tell by his brother's squinting stare that Zeke had spotted something. Dan followed his brother's stare out across the water. His eyes grew wide, his breathing heavy.

On the water, moving directly toward the boys, was a rowboat. It was strange to Dan that the boat was rowing past the point where the land began, right through the Webster's water-covered field. There were four people in the boat; as it came closer, Dan made out a man, a woman, and two small children. The man was rowing, but presently he put down his oars, stood up in the craft, and cupped his hands to his mouth.

"Dan, Zeke, can you hear me?" The man's voice quivered with exhaustion.

The boys recognized the family now. It was the Perkins family from across the river. "Yes, sir, we hear you."

The man started yelling again. "Boys, the flood water came into our house; we had to leave. We had to take our animals up on the hill beyond our meadow. Is your house safe?"

"Yes, sir, Mr. Perkins," Dan called. "Come stay with us." The Webster children had been taught by their parents to help other people whenever they could. This was a perfect opportunity. "We can make plenty of room. Row on in!"

The boys' words seemed to have relaxed Mr. Perkins. He picked up the long oar and again began to row toward the dry land where Zeke and Dan were standing. Suddenly, the boat stopped. Mr. Perkins rowed harder, but it was no use: the boat had run aground. Fifteen feet of water still separated the boat from the land. Mr. Perkins stood up and tried to propel the craft by shoving against the bottom with his oar. The boat did not budge.

"Wait, Mr. Perkins, we will push you," Zeke said. He began to remove his shoes and socks and to roll up his pant legs. Dan did the same. The boys stepped into the water.

"Goodness! This water is freezing!" The brothers hesitated for a short while until the frigidity of the water numbed their sensitive feet. Then they started again.

---

propel—*push forward*
frigidity—*extreme cold*

When they reached the boat, they pushed from the back, trying to move the uncompromising craft. But the stubborn boat did not budge an inch. "Mr. Perkins, I'm going to get Father," Dan volunteered.

"Wait, Daniel." Mr. Perkins' brightened face told the boys that he had an idea. "I am going to get out of the boat so we can try pulling on the rope in the front of the boat." Zeke and Dan waded around to the front of the boat. Mr. Perkins stepped into the water, and the three positioned themselves along the rope.

"On the count of three let's pull with all our strength!" Mr. Perkins instructed. "One . . . two . . . *THREE!*"

The three pulled mightily on the rope until the boat was completely on the land.

"Thank you, boys," Mr. Perkins said. "I never would have made it without your help. In union, there is strength."

"You're welcome, Mr. Perkins," Zeke said. "You and your family come on inside." He led them inside the warm house.

Dan stayed at the edge of the water, staring thoughtfully out over the flooded field. "In union, there is strength; in union, there is strength." He kept repeating this statement over and over in his mind. One day he would know its full meaning.

Daniel went about his regular day's work doing chores around the house.

It was very late in the afternoon when Daniel saw something else. There, coming directly toward him, was the biggest barn he had ever seen! The doors of the barn were swung wide open and Dan could see the hay in the loft. Then he heard a rooster crow, a donkey guffaw, and a cow moo.

Dan realized that the animals were in the barn. What a strange sight! He ran as fast as he could to the house and burst inside the door.

"Father, Zeke, come quickly! There is a *barn* floating on the river!"

Soon the entire family was at the water's edge, awed over the bizarre spectacle.

"It reminds me of Noah's Ark," Dan said, delighted over his comparison.

Zeke was more concerned than delighted. "How are we going to move it, Dad?"

"We will decide that in the morning, son. Let's just get the animals out for now." Mr. Webster began to closely inspect the barn. "Hm . . . It looks like John Goodrich's barn." He began to chuckle. "Zeke, ride over to the Goodrich farm and tell them that we have just discovered their barn in our backyard! Tell Mr. Goodrich to come tomorrow and bring

plenty of help. We will decide on what to do then. Hurry, son; it will be dark soon."

Dan wondered all night long what the men were going to do about the barn. The next morning he was up with the first hint of sunlight. He dressed quickly; then he went down for breakfast. As soon as he was finished, he ran outside to the water's edge. The water line had receded some, but the huge barn was still afloat, swaying gently back and forth.

After several minutes, men began to arrive at the Webster farm. Most came in ox-drawn carts filled with pick-axes, ropes, chains, and crowbars. Others rode on horseback. Soon there were several dozen men congregated near the water. Young Dan was listening intently.

"Move it? We can't move that barn!" one of the men said.

"We will have to tear it down," said another.

---

congregated—*gathered*
bickering—*disagreeing needlessly*

Soon there was arguing and bickering among the men. Each wanted to do it his own way.

Mr. Webster stood up on a nearby log and got the men's attention. Dan admired his wise father as he started to speak.

"Gentlemen, please listen. This useless arguing will get us nowhere. Now, this barn got down here in one piece; there is no reason why we can't move it back in one piece—if we work together!"

A hushed silence fell upon the group. Each man was asking himself the same question: "How?"

Mr. Webster started again. "I tell you, gentlemen, it can be done! Cyrus, lead your ox over to that corner. There is a chain there; hitch the ox to it. Amos, you hitch to the other corner."

Soon all of the oxen were hitched up to the barn by the ropes and chains. It didn't take long with everybody working together.

"Ready, men?" Mr. Webster asked. "Pull!"

At first the barn inched along, scraping against the bottom. But soon it was floating steadily up the river to its original location.

Dan was proud of his father. "That was a brilliant idea, Father. It looked impossible, but you proved otherwise!"

"Well, son, there was nothing to it once the arguing was stopped. Nothing was ever accomplished by bickering. Always remember, Dan, in union, there is strength!"

In just a few more years, Daniel Webster would become the greatest American orator and one of the ablest lawyers of his time. Daniel's lessons on "strength in union" would later have a profound influence on his life as he became a staunch supporter of national government and our country's most eloquent defender of the Union cause.

---

orator—*speaker*
profound—*of great importance*
eloquent—*able to persuade by speech*

Time to Think

1. What did Dan and Zeke see from their bedroom window when they got up?
2. What did Mr. Perkins tell the boys after they helped him pull his boat to safety?
3. What happened that proved the truth of those words?
4. How did the truth of "strength in union" influence Daniel Webster's life?

The
Star-Spangled Banner

from Francis Scott Key: God's Courageous Composer (adapted)
by David R. Collins

During the War of 1812, British troops stormed into Washington, D.C., and burned the new Capitol building. After Washington, they planned to take Fort McHenry, which guarded the entrance to Baltimore Harbor in Maryland.

When a young American lieutenant named Francis Scott Key heard that the British had captured an elderly friend of his, Dr. William Beanes, he went to President James Madison for help. Key reminded the President that Dr. Beanes had been a physician during the War for Independence. He explained that the British had made Beanes their prisoner merely because he had ordered three British soldiers arrested for drunken rowdiness.

The President wasted no time in granting Key permission to board the British flagship and ask for the release of the doctor. He wrote a note for Key to deliver to Colonel Skinner, whom he wanted to accompany Key on the mission. Knowing full well the dangers of his mission, Key rode off to find Colonel Skinner.

Francis Scott Key did not leave a written record of the alarming and inspiring events that took place next. This selection gives the story as he himself might have told it.

There was no trouble in getting cooperation for my mission. Dr. Beanes was far better known than I had thought. Everyone thought highly of the old gentleman.

"It's an outrage!" exclaimed Colonel Skinner. "The old man is guilty of nothing other than wanting his village rid of nuisances."

"I've been told Dr. Beanes is being held prisoner aboard the flagship of the British fleet," I offered.

"That would be the *Tonnant*," the Colonel replied. "The fleet is somewhere in the Chesapeake. We'll sail from Baltimore and find her."

Our horses seemed to sense the importance of our task. As we urged them faster, their steps quickened.

Baltimore steamed with excitement. The people knew British troops might land at any time and stage raids. There was also a chance the city could be attacked from the water. The British warships boasted long-range cannon.

"The city has been readying itself for weeks," Colonel Skinner explained. "Heavy cannon are placed in position at Fort McHenry."

Made of sturdy brick and wood, Fort McHenry rested comfortably at the entrance to the Baltimore harbor. It was shaped like a star.

"Perhaps you would like to visit the fort," the colonel suggested.

"I would rather complete our mission for Dr. Beanes first," I stated.

Colonel Skinner agreed.

Once our horses were taken care of, the colonel and I hurried to the Baltimore wharf. Skinner led the way to a small, narrow craft. The crew was ready for us, and we departed within an hour.

---

nuisances—*things that annoy*

"Lieutenant Key, I fancy you'll have all your fine speaking talents tested by Admiral Cockburn. He would be better suited to leading snakes and rats than men. I have never heard a kind word spoken of the man." Colonel Skinner extended some papers wrapped in a blue ribbon. "These may be of some help."

As I untied the narrow slip of cloth, I noticed the papers were letters. Each one testified to Dr. Beanes' able and kind treatment of wounds during battle. The letters were signed by British soldiers.

"These letters can certainly do us no harm," I answered.

Colonel Skinner motioned me to the side of our vessel. He pointed across the water.

"You can see how important Fort McHenry is to the defense of Baltimore," he said.

I nodded. It was not only the fort itself which impressed me. It was the giant flag of our country . . . the largest banner I had ever seen.

"Your eyes are wide," the colonel laughed. "Yes, it is quite a flag, isn't it? It measures a full thirty by forty-two feet. A young widow named Pickersgill made it. The Commandant of the fort, Major Armistead, requested a banner so large that the enemy would have no difficulty in seeing it from a distance."

"Indeed!" I laughed. "I would think the British might be able to see that banner from the shores of their own England!"

Our ship, the *Minden,* smoothly sailed through the waters of the Chesapeake. But we saw no sight of the British fleet the first day out. Success was with us on the second day.

"Ship ahoy!" a lookout called. "British ship ahoy!"

As minutes slipped away, we discovered there was not only one ship on the horizon, but many. Skinner yelled up at the lookout.

"How many can you count?"

The lookout looked through field glasses from his position. "Could be thirty-five or forty of them, Sir. They are coming this way."

Quickly, our crew ran up the flag of truce. A large battleship came closer. Colonel Skinner hailed the vessel and called out our names. We were invited to come aboard.

At first, I thought Colonel Skinner might have misjudged Admiral Cockburn. He seemed friendly enough, his stomach amply filling his uniform and his hands clenching and unclenching themselves. But once I mentioned the name of Dr. Beanes, the Admiral's face reddened. . . .

I handed Admiral Cockburn the letters. As he read, I pleaded the doctor's case.

"Dr. Beanes is a harmless man," I began. "In truth, he may not have realized the seriousness of the action he was taking in arresting your three soldiers. He is known to treat everyone he knows with respect and kindness, perhaps much like yourself . . ."

On I went, and on further. As I spoke, I remembered how I would sometimes flatter my sister Ann to gain special favors. It had all worked well until my mother had told my sister the words from the Good Book: *He shall come in peaceably, and obtain the kingdom by flatteries.* It was Daniel 11:21, I believe. Thankfully, the admiral seemed to enjoy remarks aimed to suit his vanity.

As he read, our host's manner mellowed. The letters were passed to his other officers dining with us. Their reactions seemed positive. By the time Skinner and I left his quarters that evening, I was convinced Dr. Beanes was to be a free man.

My feelings proved true enough. We received word that Dr. Beanes was to be released to us.

"Now, if we can only sail away from here swiftly," Colonel Skinner said softly. "There is much movement afoot. Whispers run rampant."

I had noticed this as well. Sailors were constantly active, never stopping to look our way. I hoped the Minden could return us to Baltimore as safely as she had brought us to the Tonnant.

But as we were leaving the flagship, a British officer hurried to us.

"I'm sorry, gentlemen," the Englishman said firmly. "You will be returned to your own ship at once. We will furnish you with a crew. For the time being, though, you will sail with us."

106

"We do not choose to remain," I answered. "Why are you detaining us?"

The officer looked at me with narrowed eyes.

"Sir, we are about to attack Baltimore. You will remain with the fleet until the battle is over."

I swallowed deeply. I felt as if this were a bad dream, a horrible nightmare from which I would soon awaken.

"But we've come to you under a flag of truce!" Colonel Skinner protested.

"You will not be harmed in any way," the officer answered. "The three of you will be taken back to your ship until the fighting is over and we have secured Baltimore."

"You sound very certain of yourself," I snapped. "What if your attack should fail?"

The British officer stared at me, his eyes revealing a total disgust. Suddenly he turned to a few of his sailors standing nearby.

"Return these men to the *Minden* at once!" he ordered.

The orders were obeyed. An hour later, we stood on the deck of our own ship, sailing up the bay with the British fleet.

"This is outrageous!" Dr. Beanes declared. "They broke into my home and dragged me from my bed. They kept me in irons. Now they make me a witness to an attack on my own country."

I felt just as angry as the good doctor, but a sick feeling ate at my stomach as well. Here I was, a lieutenant in the United States Army, aboard an enemy ship. An attack was going to be launched against my people, my nation, and I was helpless to stop it.

---

detaining—*holding back*

107

Colonel Skinner cast a comforting arm around my shoulder. His eyes were misty.

"I know what you're feeling, my friend, but there is nothing we can do."

". . . nothing we can do." The words struck a familiar chord in my memory. It brought back a vision of Grandmother Key as I read to her. It was a horrid rainy afternoon, and I could not go outside. I had wanted to explore a woods nearby and ride a horse.

"Well," Grandmother had said, "the rain is here, and there is nothing we can do about it. But we can always pray together. Remember, Francis, you can always pray, even by yourself. That is always something you can do. . . ."

So, on that night of September 13, 1814, I stood on board the *Minden* and prayed. I watched as the ships in the fleet formed halfcircles around the fort. British gunners awaited the signal to fire. When it came, the thunder of shells rumbled across the bay.

Our ship was outside of reach when the fort returned the enemy's fire. Sadly enough, the shells from the fort fell short. It was clear the British had our own troops outgunned.

Ca-boom! Boom! Ca-boom! The bombs and rockets pounded the fort. Heavy smoke from the burned powder filled the bay.

"Is the flag still flying over the fort?" Dr. Beanes asked. "I cannot see that far."

I strained to see through the smoke. Yes, the flag was still flying. Thank God it was such a huge banner!

"Yes, Doctor, it still flies."

"Let us hope it will remain flying," Colonel Skinner said softly. "If it falls, it means the fort has surrendered."

"The city will no longer be free," the doctor said. "I pray those brave men in the fort can hold out."

I watched the doctor shuffle away, disappearing into the darkness. My heart ached for him. He still carried memories of the War of Independence battles. Now he was a witness to this.

From my pocket I took an envelope. So often in the past I had jotted down a few lines for a poem which I completed later. Now I scribbled a few words and phrases. America was a land of brave and free people. The flag symbolized that freedom, that courage. The words came quickly.

My head pounded with the sound of exploding shots and shells. Waves slapped against the sides of the *Minden,* raising and lowering the craft in the water. Boom! Ca-boom! The rockets lit up the sky with their glare. Again I scribbled my impressions.

I paced along the deck, aware that I was surrounded by hostile sailors. They were hoping for the fort to fall just as strongly as I prayed for it to hold. The smoke grew so thick we could no longer even see the giant banner of our country. Maryland had called upon its sons to defend that flag and our nation. I prayed for their success.

Rain began to fall. The ships moved closer to the fort. Then Fort McHenry cut loose with all its guns. Boom! Ca-boom! I coughed violently, choking on the heavy smoke.

110

Without warning, the firing stopped. The air was still. How I longed to see the fort! Was the flag still flying? Or perhaps the stars and stripes have given way to the British banner.

"What's happened?" Doctor Beanes asked, stumbling up on the deck. "Has the fort surrendered?"

"We don't know," I answered. "We can't know until sunrise."

Time crawled. We stood waiting in the darkness. My mouth felt dusty and dry. Dampness covered my body as the rain mingled with my own body moisture.

"The sun's coming up," Colonel Skinner murmured. "The dawn is breaking."

Once more I took out my envelopes. I scribbled away, noting the glow of the dawn's early light. The mist had cleared away the smoke.

"I can see it!" I exclaimed. "The flag—our flag—it's still there!"

The doctor grabbed my arm. He leaned across the railing, trying desperately to see.

"Are you sure it is *our* flag, Francis?"

"Yes, yes!" I answered. "It is ours! It's our beloved red, white, and blue. May God be praised!"

My hand raced across the envelope, recording what

I felt and what I was seeing. The sailors moved around us, preparing to leave. Soon the British crew left the ship, and our own sailors took over. Joyfully, we watched the enemy ships sail away.

"They've given up," I exclaimed. "We've won!"

Within hours, the *Minden* was headed for the wharf in the Baltimore harbor. The thoughts of a warm meal and a clean bed filled my head. But there was something I had to do first.

Once we found a room in a Baltimore inn, Doctor Beanes and Colonel Skinner ate a hearty meal and headed for bed. I joined them for the meal, but I asked the innkeeper for paper, ink, and quill when I went to my room.

By the soft light of the morning, I began to write.

Francis Scott Key had no idea that the poem he wrote during those trying hours would live on today as our National Anthem.

O! say can you see by the dawn's early light,
What so proudly we hail'd at the twilight's last gleaming?
Whose broad stripes and bright stars, thro' the perilous fight,
O'er the ramparts we watched were so gallantly streaming?
And the rocket's red glare, the bombs bursting in air,
Gave proof thro' the night that our flag was still there;
O! say does that star-spangled banner yet wave
O'er the land of the free and the home of the brave?

On the shore, dimly seen through the mists of the deep,
Where the foe's haughty host in dread silence reposes,
What is that which the breeze, o'er the towering steep,
As it fitfully blows, half conceals, half discloses?

---

ramparts—*forts*

Now it catches the gleam of the morning's first beam,
In full glory reflected, now shines on the steam;
'Tis the star-spangled banner, O! long may it wave
O'er the land of the free and the home of the brave!

O! thus be it ever when free men shall stand
Between their loved home and the war's desolation;
Blest with vict'ry and peace, may the Heav'n-rescued land
Praise the Pow'r that hath made and preserved us a nation!
Then conquer we must, when our cause it is just;
And this be our motto, "In God is our trust!"
And the star-spangled banner in triumph shall wave
O'er the land of the free and the home of the brave!

---

desolation—*destruction*

Time to Think

1. Why did Mr. Key get on board the British flagship?
2. What did Mr. Key notice about the flag flying over Fort McHenry?
3. What was Mr. Key forced to do that troubled him so much?
4. What time of day was it when Mr. Key wrote "The Star-Spangled Banner"?
5. Was "The Star-Spangled Banner" originally written as our national anthem?

Respecting
the Flag

from the booklet Our Flag *published by the U.S. Congress*

★ When the flag is displayed during rendition of the National Anthem or recital of the Pledge of Allegiance, all present except those in uniform should stand at attention facing the flag with the right hand over the heart. (Those in uniform salute the flag as they would an officer.)

★ It is the universal custom to display the flag only from sunrise to sunset on buildings and on stationary flagstaffs in the open. However, when a patriotic effect is desired, the flag may be displayed twenty-four hours a day if properly illuminated during the hours of darkness.

★ The flag should be hoisted briskly and lowered ceremoniously.

rendition—*a performance*
illuminated—*lit up*
inclement—*stormy*

★ The flag should not be displayed on days when the weather is inclement, except when an all-weather flag is displayed.

★ The flag should be displayed daily on or near the main administration building of every public institution.

★ The flag should be displayed in or near every polling place on election days.

★ The flag should be displayed during school days in or near every schoolhouse.

★ The flag of the United States of America should be at the center and at the highest point of the group when a number of flags of states or localities, or pennants of societies, are grouped and displayed from staffs.

★ The flag should never be displayed with the union (the blue field) down, except as a signal of dire distress in instances of extreme danger to life or property.

★ The flag should never touch anything beneath it, such as the ground, the floor, water, or merchandise. The flag may be used to cover a casket, but it should not be lowered into the grave or allowed to touch the ground.

★ The flag should never be carried flat or horizontally, but always aloft and free.

★ The flag should never be used as wearing apparel, bedding, or drapery.

---

dire—*extreme*

Time to Think ————————————————————————

1. When is it proper to salute a flag?
2. Near what buildings should the flag be displayed?
3. Describe how the flag should be carried?
4. Would it be proper to drape the flag over a piece of furniture for decoration? Why not?

Cyrus Hall McCormick Invents the Reaping Machine

Elizabeth Watson

This is the true story of a man named Cyrus Hall McCormick, who as a boy lived on a farm in the Shenandoah Valley in the beautiful Blue Ridge Mountains of Virginia.

At that time almost everyone in the United States lived on a farm, and a great many of those farms were in the valleys along the rivers and streams that flowed to the sea. In those days there were only a few roads in the entire country, and those roads were so narrow, so rough, and so full of tree stumps and deep mud holes that people would not use them if they could possibly travel by water. Everyone tried to live near a river or stream, on which boats could be used to carry the corn, wheat, flax, and wool down to the market towns on the coast, where they could be traded for the salt, iron, tea, tools, and other things that were needed.

---

flax—*plant stems used to make cloth*

116

Great-grandfather McCormick had lived on a farm in Pennsylvania. On this farm he plowed and harvested the grain with the farm tools he had brought with him from his home in Europe. In those early days there were no machines such as we have today to help with the farm work; in fact, farmers were just beginning to discover new ways of making hand tools which could do more work than the old tools their forefathers had used.

These farm tools were centuries old. The plow with which Great-grandfather McCormick broke his ground, and the sickles with which he cut his grain, were like the plows and sickles the farmers of Egypt thousands of years before had used on their farms along the banks of the Nile River. The short scythes used on the McCormick place were almost exactly like the scythes used on the old farms of Rome.

When Great-grandfather McCormick's son grew up and wanted a farm of his own, there was little good land left on any of the rivers or streams near his father's home. So Son McCormick took his tools and went off across the Indian trails running through the forest and over the hills and came out on the banks of the Shenandoah River in Virginia. Here there was still plenty of land to be had for nothing. He cut down trees, built himself a log house, then plowed and planted his newly cleared land with corn and wheat. The land was rich, and it grew splendid crops. Everything went well with the young McCormick family. As time went on, the family grew bigger and bigger. As the McCormick family grew, the farm spread out over more and more land.

---

sickle—*a curved blade used for cutting grain*
scythe—*a curved blade used for reaping*

This Virginia farm had great fields of oats, corn, wheat, and other grains; beautiful pastures with strong, fine horses, good cows, and fleecy sheep; and large barnyards of hens, ducks, and geese. There were two gristmills for grinding McCormicks' and their neighbors' grain into flour and meal. Two sawmills quickly turned logs into broad planks and stout boards. A smelting furnace turned iron ore from the nearby mountain into lumps of pure iron all ready for the farm's blacksmith to hammer and beat into horseshoes, pincers, tongs, crowbars, hammers, and other tools needed on the farm. They spun and wove their own cloth and made it into clothing; they made their own soap and candles, dyes, barrels, tubs, and vats. In fact, the McCormick family, like all other farmers of the time, did everything for themselves.

Every year they plowed and planted great fields of corn, wheat, and oats. And every year when the grain was ripe, every man, woman, and child of the McCormick family went out into the grain fields to help bring in their winter's food.

The harvest season was so short that there was not a single minute to waste if the precious grain was to be put under cover before the fall storms came. Rain, wind, and sunshine were good for grain all through the long months of the growing season, but rain, wind, and too much sunshine were anything but good for grain that was tall and ripe. And so the moment the grain was ripe enough to be cut, the whole family went into the fields and worked from daylight until dark. They hastened to get their harvest in before the storms overtook them, or before the warm sun over-ripened the seeds, so that they fell to the ground to be blown away by the slightest breezes.

pincers—*large tongs with jawlike ends*

118

The men with sickles went ahead. They held a bunch of grain with one hand, swung the sickle with the other, and let the stalks fall to the ground as they cut their way across the field. Each man with a sickle was followed by another worker who gathered up the fallen stalks, tied them into bundles, and tossed them back to the ground. The men who had the scythes with the long handles and blades did not need to hold the grain as they cut it. They used both hands to swing the scythe, and they cut a wider path through the grain as they worked their way across the fields.

The tools that Son McCormick and his neighbors used in harvesting their crops were the same as those used by Great-grandfather McCormick on his farm back in Pennsylvania.

After using such tools for many years, Son McCormick bought a scythe he had seen the farmers along the coast using to harvest their grain. They called the new kind of scythe a cradle scythe because it had long wooden fingers on the handle just above the knife. These fingers cradled, or held the grain until the knife had finished its work, then laid it in neat rows at one side.

Fifty years went by, and the sons and grandsons of the first McCormick who had settled in the Shenandoah Valley were still harvesting their grain with the cradle scythe. One of the McCormick sons spent every spare moment of his time in his workshop. There he had discovered several new ways of making many of the old farm tools into new tools which did a great deal more work than any of the old ones had ever been able to do. But try as he would, he could *not* find any better or quicker way of cutting the ripe grain.

As he went about the country and saw field after field of ripe grain that could not possibly be cut and gathered in time to save it, he began to see that men with *hand tools* alone could not keep up with the huge crops the rich farmlands were producing. Some kind of harvesting *machine* was needed. So he began to study and plan and work. When his machine was finally finished, he and his son Cyrus Hall McCormick tried it out in one of their fields. Something went wrong; it trampled down the grain instead of cutting it.

Then Cyrus Hall McCormick began experimenting with his father's machine. After many trials he sent out word one day to the farmers that he had made a reaping machine. He invited them to come and see it work. More than a hundred neighbors gathered at Farmer Ruff's field, where the machine was to be tried out. The reaping machine rattled and clattered as Cyrus Hall McCormick drove it out of the barn and into the field. Dogs barked and boys yelled and whistled through their fingers as the machine rattled clumsily along. The slaves chuckled and laughed; farmers grinned and shook their heads in disbelief. They did not believe that such an awkward-looking machine could ever cut grain, and they did not hesitate to say what they thought.

The field was rough and hilly. Jolting and jerking from side to side, the reaping machine cut the grain in such irregular fashion that Farmer Ruff ordered Cyrus Hall McCormick to stop the horses and cease ruining his field of wheat. A bystander shouted to McCormick, "Pull down that fence; drive over into my field and try your machine there." In that field, which was smooth and level, Cyrus Hall McCormick's machine cut six acres of oats easily before the sun went down!

The new machine could do all the work of cutting grain. It had a divider that separated the grain to be cut from the grain left standing. It had fingers that caught and held the stalks while the knife blade moved back and forth, cutting with each stroke. In fact, it had all the main parts of the reaping machines we use on our farms today. The McCormick farm of the Shenandoah Valley had made history.

Our present-day harvester cuts off the heads of wheat, threshes it, separates husks from grain, weighs the grain, and dumps it into a holding tank. Since it combines the work of several machines, it is called a combine. It is self-powered or pulled by a tractor rather than by horses. This great machine owes its beginning to Cyrus Hall McCormick's clumsy old reaping machine.

---

threshes—*separates grain and seed from straw*

Time to Think

1. What kind of tools did the McCormick family use to harvest crops before Cyrus invented the reaper?
2. Why didn't the neighbors think Cyrus's machine would work?
3. How did Cyrus prove to the neighbors that his machine could be useful?
4. How did Cyrus McCormick's machine influence agriculture?

"Remember the Alamo!"

Norman Richards

In the 1830s and 1840s, Texas was owned and held by Mexico, under the bloody and brutal rule of Santa Anna, the military leader and president of Mexico. Santa Anna was a very able leader, but cruel and treacherous. He hated the American colonists and ruled them like a tyrant. The Americans who defended the Alamo were as fine and brave a people as ever lived, and their fight for liberty forms one of the brightest pages of American history.

While Santa Anna's army of 5,000 soldiers was marching toward Texas, a band of 300 volunteers attacked the Mexican troops who were using the abandoned Alamo mission as a fort. The Texas volunteers fought so hard that the Mexicans retreated and left the Alamo and the whole town of San Antonio to them. Buck Travis and Jim Bowie each arrived at the Alamo with a group of armed volunteers.

On the morning of February 8, 1836, the people in San Antonio and the Alamo cheered to welcome a special visitor, Davy Crockett, the most famous frontiersman in the world.

---

treacherous—*dangerous*   **tyrant**—*a cruel ruler*

Davy Crockett was said to be the best rifle shot in the world. People said he could shoot the string of a kite in half when it was flying in a high wind. The men in the Alamo wanted to make Crockett a colonel in the volunteers. "No, I'll just be kind of a high private," Davy told them. He carried his famous rifle, "Old Betsy."

There were now almost two hundred men in the Alamo, but they knew they would need help from many more men if Santa Anna's army attacked. They hoped they could hold out until help arrived.

Jim Bowie ordered a sentry to stay in the tall tower of a church in the town to watch for the Mexican army. Finally, at dawn on the morning of February 23, 1836, the sentry spotted a huge mass of men far off on the horizon. It was Santa Anna's army. The sentry rang the bell with all his strength, and the Texas volunteers hurried into the Alamo. The long-awaited fight was coming.

Santa Anna set up headquarters in the town of San Antonio. He sent a messenger to the Alamo, telling the Texans to surrender. They refused. Then he sent word that he would take no prisoners when the fort was captured. Everyone inside would be killed.

The Mexicans surrounded the Alamo and dug trenches for soldiers, but when they dared to come close to the fort, Davy Crockett picked them off with deadly aim. Even though many of their soldiers were killed, the Mexicans kept bringing their cannon closer and closer to the Alamo.

Santa Anna ordered the cannon to open fire. From then on there was a constant roar, day and night, as the guns blasted the fort. The Texans held their fire to save ammunition, knowing that, with fewer than two hundred men, they could not fight off Santa Anna's thousands of troops forever. They would need their ammunition if the Mexicans came pouring over the walls.

---

picked them off—*shot them one by one*

In the days that followed, Santa Anna's soldiers rushed toward the Alamo again and again. Each time, the Texans' deadly fire was so accurate that the attacks failed. Davy Crockett from his post at the wall sent many enemy soldiers running for safety. Santa Anna's men had never seen such fierce fighters as these trapped Texans.

Jim Bowie had injured his leg and then caught pneumonia. Soon he had a high fever and grew weaker and weaker. After a few days, he had to lie on a cot in one of the rooms, too ill to fight anymore. Buck Travis took command of the whole group of volunteers and continued to lead the defense. The Mexicans kept firing day and night, and the men in the Alamo could not take time to sleep. Every man was needed at his post on the wall, no matter how tired he was.

Buck Travis sent messages to leaders in other parts of Texas, begging for help. "I shall never surrender or retreat," he wrote; "VICTORY or DEATH."

When big Sam Houston got word that the Alamo was surrounded and under attack, he set out with Regular Army troops to rescue it, but it was a long march. It would take days to get there.

Meanwhile, the tired defenders of the Alamo were running lower and lower on ammunition. With every attack, the troops of Santa Anna managed to get closer and closer to the walls of the fort. The men inside knew now that help would not come in time. They knew they were going to die, but they vowed to fight to the end to prevent Santa Anna from taking over Texas. They were willing to give their lives for liberty, just as Americans had before them. Their flag, flying atop the highest wall, was the flag of Mexico with the words

"Constitution of 1824" lettered in the middle. They wanted to be good citizens of a free Mexico to the end.

After many days of pounding, the Mexican cannon finally blasted a huge hole in the north wall of the old mission. Other cannon kept firing at the other walls. The defenders inside kept fighting back bravely, but it was getting more dangerous all the time.

In the meantime, a group of Texas leaders met at a convention many miles away in a town called Washington-on-the-Brazos. They decided that Texans could no longer live under the tyranny of Santa Anna, and they declared, as representatives of the people, that Texas was now independent from Mexico. They set up a Republic of Texas and chose a temporary president until the war with Santa Anna was over.

On the night of March 5, the guns of Santa Anna's army fell silent. The tired defenders in the Alamo tried to get some sleep to be ready for the next attack. Santa Anna was clever; he knew the Texans were so exhausted they would find it hard to wake up again.

The time for the final attack had come. At five o' clock the next morning, thousands of Mexican troops rushed the Alamo. They flung ladders up against the walls so they could climb over. The weary Texans struggled to awaken and grab their guns. Manning the top of the walls, they put up a fierce fight, killing as many as seven enemy soldiers for every one of them that died. But there were too many enemy troops. And more and more kept coming. One by one, the brave defenders died fighting.

---

convention—*a large meeting*

Twice the troops of Santa Anna were driven back, but more soldiers were sent to attack again. Finally there were so few defenders left that the Mexicans came pouring over the walls. Buck Travis died at the cannon he was firing. Then Davy Crockett fell dead, surrounded by enemy dead. The Texans fought with clubs, knives, and anything else they had, but they were overwhelmed. Santa Anna's troops rushed into the room where Jim Bowie lay sick on his cot and killed him. At last there were no more defenders alive. The brave fight was over.

Sam Houston was on his way to the Alamo with his troops when a messenger gave him the news that the Alamo had fallen. Santa Anna was marching toward the towns along the Gulf of Mexico, planning to conquer all of Texas. The Mexican general felt sure the Texans would be so frightened that they would surrender and give up their ideas of freedom, but when Houston and all the other people of Texas heard about the brave fight put up by the men in the Alamo, they were more determined than ever to fight Santa Anna and win freedom.

In the following weeks, Santa Anna marched his men across Texas, chasing after the leaders of the new Texas government. Sam Houston retreated, but he kept adding men to his army, and it grew bigger.

At last Houston saw his chance. Santa Anna and his troops were camped on a peninsula on the coast, where they could be trapped. Houston rushed with eight hundred men, marching day and night, until he reached the spot where the enemy was. His scouts destroyed the bridge over which Santa Anna might escape. He was trapped.

It was broad daylight, and the Mexican soldiers were not expecting an attack by any large group. Suddenly, Sam Houston yelled to his men, "Trust in God and fear not! Victory is certain! Remember the Alamo!" That was all the furious Texans needed. They attacked fiercely. Charging, shooting, and swinging swords, they overwhelmed the Mexican troops. In a short time they had completely defeated the enemy, and the Mexicans surrendered.

All except Santa Anna, that is. The wily general managed to escape on a fast horse in the confusion of the battle. He changed his uniform for some plain work clothes and tried to hide out, but he was soon discovered and brought back to Sam Houston as a prisoner. Houston had been shot in the ankle and lay propped up against a tree when Santa Anna was

---

wily—*sly; full of tricks*

brought to him. With bitter memories of the men killed at the Alamo, he could have ordered the enemy general shot. But Houston was not as cruel as Santa Anna, and he decided to let the general live and go back to Mexico.

First, though, Santa Anna had to agree to sign a treaty recognizing Texas as a free and independent republic. He also had to agree to remove his army from Texas and not come back again. Santa Anna signed quickly and was glad to escape alive after all the cruel things he had done.

There was great celebrating all over Texas, for at last the people were free to live under a representative government. Sam Houston was a hero, and the people elected him President of the Republic of Texas. They also voted to ratify a constitution that guaranteed freedom.

Texas remained an independent country until 1845. Then the people voted to join the United States, and it became the state of Texas. Texans and other Americans have always remembered the Alamo and the brave men who died there. They fought so that others might have freedom, and the battle of the Alamo will always be a shining chapter in history.

---

ratify—*approve*

Time to Think

1. How many men defended the Alamo against Santa Anna's 5,000 soldiers?

2. What famous frontiersman joined the fight at the Alamo?

3. In what town did this story take place?

4. Why didn't the Texans fire their weapons often even though Santa Anna's men kept moving closer?

5. What cruel plan did Santa Anna use to finally defeat the Texans?

6. What did Sam Houston tell his men that helped them to defeat the Mexicans?

7. What did the defenders of the Alamo achieve even though they died fighting?

Our Country

John G. Whittier

O! make Thou us through centuries long,
    In peace secure, in justice strong;
Around our gift of freedom draw
    The safeguards of Thy righteous law.

---

safeguards—*things that protect*

The Oregon Trail

Arthur Guiterman

Two hundred wagons, rolling out to Oregon,

Breaking through the gopher holes, lurching wide and free,

Crawling up the mountain pass, jolting, grumbling, rumbling on,

Two hundred wagons, rolling to the sea.

From East and South and North they flocked, to muster, row on row,

A fleet of ten score prairie ships beside Missouri's flow,

The bull whips crack, the oxen strain, the canvas-hooded files

Are off upon the long, long trail of sixteen hundred miles.

The women hold the guiding-lines; beside the rocking steers

With goad and ready rifle walk the bearded pioneers

Through clouds of dust beneath the sun; through floods
   of sweeping rain,

Across the Kansas prairie land, across Nebraska's plain.

Two hundred wagons, rolling out to Oregon,

Curved around the campfire flame at halt when day is done,

Rest awhile beneath the stars, yoke again and lumber on,

Two hundred wagons, rolling with the sun.

---

muster—*gather*
goad—*a pointed rod used to urge animals along*

Among the barren buttes they wind beneath the jealous view
Of Blackfoot, Pawnee, Omaha, Arapahoe, and Sioux.
No savage threat may check their course, no river deep and wide;
They swim the Platte, they ford the Snake, they cross the Great Divide.
They march as once from India's vales through Asia's mountain door
With shield and spear on Europe's plain their fathers marched before.
They march where leap the antelope and storm the buffalo,
Still Westward as their fathers marched [so many] years ago.

Two hundred wagons, rolling out to Oregon,
Creeping down the dark defile below the mountain crest,
Surging through the brawling stream, lunging, plunging, forging on,
Two hundred wagons, rolling toward the West.

Now toils the dusty caravan with swinging wagon poles
Where Walla Walla pours along, where broad Columbia rolls.
The long-haired trapper's face grows dark and scowls the painted brave;
Where now the beaver builds his dam the wheat and rye shall wave.
The British trader shakes his head and weighs his nation's loss,
For where those hardy settlers come the Stars and Stripes will toss.

---

buttes—*hills that have flat tops*
Arapahoe (ə·răp′ə·hō)
Sioux (sōō)
Platte (plăt)

vales—*valleys*
defile—*a narrow passageway*
crest—*the very top*
Walla Walla (wŏl′ə wŏl′ə)

Then block the wheels, unyoke the steers, the prize is his who dares;

The cabin rise, the fields are sown, and Oregon is theirs!

They will take, they will hold,

By the spade in the mold,

By the seed in the soil,

By the sweat and the toil,

By the plow in the loam,

By the school and the home!

Two hundred wagons, rolling out to Oregon,

Two hundred wagons, ranging free and far,

Two hundred wagons, rumbling, grumbling, rolling on,

Two hundred wagons, following a Star!

---

loam—*soil*

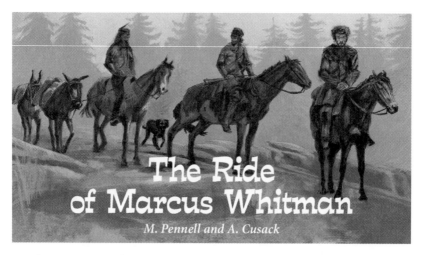

The Ride
of Marcus Whitman

M. Pennell and A. Cusack

"Hurrah for Oregon! America is too late! The country is ours!" shouted a young Englishman.

A messenger had just brought the news to the Hudson's Bay Company's fort that a group of Englishmen and Canadians were on their way to settle in the valley of the Columbia River. In the year 1842, the western boundary line between Canada and the United States had not yet been determined, but it was believed that whichever country settled the land first, that country would have the title to it.

Marcus Whitman, an American missionary doctor to the Indians of Oregon, heard the triumphant cry of the Englishman. He was planning a four-thousand-mile journey to the East on mission work, and now he determined to start at once, although winter was coming. He felt that it was important to make Congress realize the value of this Western territory and to get American settlers at once for Oregon. He wanted this land to belong to his country, and he wanted to be free to continue his missionary work there.

The name "Oregon" at that time meant not only the present state, but also the land now occupied by the states of

Washington, Idaho, and part of Montana. The Hudson's Bay Company, with England's approval, had planted their forts in various places in this territory, and they were doing their best to keep American settlers away. The people in the territory knew that the land was well worth cultivating, and that there was plenty of fish and game in the rivers and forests, and possibilities of ores in the mountains. In the East, however, the people had obtained the impression that the country was impassable and not worth struggling to keep, as it was full of wild beasts and Indians.

Marcus Whitman, who had lived in Oregon for six years, realized what a tremendous loss to the United States it would be if the boundary line were fixed below the forty-ninth parallel. If this should happen, it would give the land to England. So on October 3, 1842, Marcus Whitman said good-bye to his wife and friends. With General Lovejoy, who was a new settler, a guide, and three pack mules, he began his long journey to Washington to persuade the President and Congress to keep Oregon.

In eleven days the party reached Fort Hall, where the captain of the fort tried to prevent the doctor from going any farther. He told the travelers that it was hopeless to try to journey over the Rocky Mountains, as the snow was already twenty feet deep. He said that two tribes of Indians were at war with each other, and that it would be certain death to pass through their country.

In spite of this discouraging news, Dr. Whitman would not return home, but he changed his route and set out toward the southeast to discover a new way to Washington.

---

ores—*minerals that contain metal*

He knew the route in a general way, though it was believed that no white man had ever taken it. He went first east and south in the direction of the present Salt Lake City, then to Fort Uintah and Fort Uncompahgre, on to Taos and Santa Fe, and from there to Bent's Fort and St. Louis.

The deep snow and severe weather delayed the men, but they safely reached Fort Uncompahgre on the Rio Grande and from there took a new guide. On their way to Taos they had to pass over a high mountain, and here a terrible snowstorm made them seek shelter in a more protected ravine. They tried several times to go on, but it was ten days before they could leave. They had no sooner got upon the mountain again, than another violent storm almost blinded them.

Uintah (yo͞o·ĭnt′ə)
Uncompahgre (ŭn′kəm·pä′grē)
ravine—*a deep valley caused by water*

138

Fighting every step of the way through the stinging, whirling snow, they struggled on. Finally the guide stopped and said that he was lost and would go no farther. They decided to return to the camp in the sheltered ravine where they had been, but the snow had covered every sign of the path by which they had come. The guide could not direct them. They seemed utterly lost on top of the mountain in the wild storm.

Then it was that Dr. Whitman got down from his horse, knelt in the snow, and prayed. He commended his life work, his family, and Oregon to God for guidance and protection.

The lead mule, left to himself while the doctor was praying, turned its long ears first one way and then another and then started plunging through the snowdrifts.

"This mule will find the camp if it can live long enough to reach it," said the guide. The men followed the mule, and they all reached the camp safely.

"I will go no farther. The way is impassable," the guide declared. The party could not go on without a guide, so Dr. Whitman rode back to the fort and engaged a new guide. In a week they were ready to start again.

When the party reached the place where they must cross the Grand River, they found two hundred feet of solid ice on each side of the stream with a rushing torrent in between.

"It is too dangerous to attempt to cross," decided the guide.

"We must cross, and we must cross now!" said Dr. Whitman.

He cut a willow pole eight feet long and put it upon his shoulder. "Now shove me off," he commanded. General Lovejoy and the guide obeyed. Both horse and rider went out of sight, but they soon reappeared swimming. When they reached the other shore, the doctor dismounted, broke the ice with his pole, and then helped the horse out. He soon had a roaring fire, and when the general and the guide got safely over with the pack mules, they all spent the day in getting dry and warm.

From there on the little group of travelers had many delays and suffered severely from the cold. Although every care was taken, Dr. Whitman's feet, hands, and ears were frozen. Before they reached Santa Fe the party had run short of supplies. At Santa Fe the doctor stopped only long enough to get supplies, for he realized that he must hasten.

When the party reached the Arkansas River they found grass for the horses and were able to get game for food, so they pushed quickly onward. One day after a long, hard ride

they decided to camp by one of the tributaries of the river.
There was plenty of wood for a fire on the other side, but
none on their side. The river was frozen over with smooth,
clear ice, which was hardly thick enough to hold a man.
They must have wood, however, so the doctor took the ax,
lay down on the ice, and carefully crawled across. He cut a
load of wood, and on his return pushed it before him. He
reached the others in safety, but in cutting the wood he had
split the ax helve. An ax is a very important article in the
woods, and so it was at once mended by binding the helve
together with a fresh deerskin thong. The next morning the
ax could not be found. A hungry wolf had probably wanted
the deerskin for his dinner and had taken ax and all, as it lay
at the edge of the tent. Although the men managed to get
along without it, it is doubtful if they could have proceeded
had the ax been lost during the first part of their journey.

---

tributaries—*streams that flow into a larger body of water*

There were several more delays, for traveling through the woods in the winter was difficult. There was one particularly anxious week when Dr. Whitman, hurrying ahead to join a caravan starting for St. Louis, got lost on the way. When he returned, General Lovejoy, who was not well, remained at one of the forts, but Dr. Whitman hurried on to St. Louis.

When he reached the city, he was surrounded by trappers and traders eager for news and curious about his journey, but his first thought was about the treaty. He found that it had been signed, but only the boundary of a few acres in Maine had been settled. The doctor would not stay in St. Louis, for his great purpose was to get to Washington before Congress adjourned. The river was frozen, and he had to go on the stagecoach rather than by boat. It was a hard journey for a man already tired, but he did not hesitate.

When he got to Washington, President Tyler and Secretary of State Daniel Webster quickly granted him an audience.

At this time Marcus Whitman was about forty-one years old. He was a man of medium height, with broad shoulders and a large head covered with iron-gray hair. He wore coarse fur garments—buckskin breeches, fur leggings, and boot moccasins, and he carried a buffalo overcoat. He stood before the President, a sturdy pioneer, a missionary doctor, who had dared to travel four thousand miles over a rough country in winter. It had taken him four months to make the trip. He asked for no money or land or office to pay him for his four months of travel. He pleaded only for the saving of Oregon, because it would add to his country's wealth and to the benefit of the hardy pioneers who were already on their homesteads in the West.

granted an audience—*listened*

"But Oregon is a barren, worthless territory," objected Daniel Webster. "It is shut off from the rest of the country by impassable mountains and by a great desert which make the building of a wagon road an impossibility. Without wagons people cannot farm the land and build themselves homes."

"That is not true," replied Marcus Whitman. "I have taken my wagon over the road. The soil is wonderful, and the climate is delightful. I have grown a variety of crops successfully."

The President and the Secretary of State listened intently while the doctor described the land to them and mentioned its rich possibilities. Whitman reminded them that it had been said that the ownership of Oregon would very likely be given to the country that had the greater number of settlers, English or American. "All I ask," he said, "is that you won't barter away Oregon or allow English interference before I can lead a band of sturdy Americans across the plains to make their homes on the land."

His request was granted. Both countries had claimed the territory; but now, when the story of Marcus Whitman's ride became generally known, the interest of Americans was aroused. They were determined not to lose the land.

After Dr. Whitman had attended to his business relating to the missions, he began to gather together a group of pioneers to return to Oregon with him. A year from the time when he had started on his long, hard ride he had reached his home again. With him came one hundred twenty-five wagons, one thousand head of cattle, horses, and sheep, and about one thousand men, women, and children.

144

Thus Oregon was settled by Americans, who not only outnumbered the English, but who came as permanent settlers intending to farm the land and build homes, rather than as trappers or traders.

After many delays, threats of war, and various negotiations, an agreement was reached which satisfied both England and America, and on July 17,1846, both governments signed the treaty which fixed the boundary line between the United States and Canada at the forty-ninth parallel. Thus another chapter in the story of a great nation was written.

---

negotiations—*discussions held in order to reach a decision*

Time to Think

1. Why did Dr. Whitman make such a long journey to Washington?
2. What were some of the struggles Dr. Whitman and his friends faced along the journey?
3. Why did Daniel Webster object to Dr. Whitman's plea to save Oregon?
4. What did Dr. Whitman do when he was granted permission to claim the territory for the United States?
5. Name some of the benefits we enjoy today because of Dr. Whitman's perseverance.

The Bible Rides the Western Plains

Grace W. McGavran

United States (1860)

Before telegraph poles stretched across the country, Americans needed a fast way to get mail from coast to coast. That way would be the Pony Express. Boys and young men were needed to speed the mail on horseback from one post to another. A Pony Express rider had to be more than just a good horseman; he had to be alert, resourceful, and a person of the highest character. Would Charles Martin, the young frontiersman and guide, meet those qualifications? Mr. Majors, one of the backers of the enterprise, knew how to find out.

Young Charles slipped from his horse's back as the little company of riders came to a stop below the crest of the hill. Up over the hill ahead of them went the faint trail.

"Wait here!" Charles ordered curtly, and the others waited. They did not mind, because they understood the reason.

Again and again as Charles had guided them across the almost trackless plain the same thing had happened. Charles was taking no chances on meeting Apache warriors, or on riding into a nest of bandits with the men he was convoying across the western plains. Not for nothing was he known as one of the keenest and the toughest of the young plainsmen. Folk felt safe if Charles Martin undertook to guide them where they wanted to go.

Charles moved silently up the hillside. Stooping behind a shrubby tree near the crest, he crept forward. A moment later he was gone from sight. Many a time had he spied out the land from beneath the cover of a stunted bit of growth along the lonely trail.

Presently he strode down the slope and swung into his saddle. "Plains clear as far as the eye can see," he said briefly. The horses started and the long journey across the plains continued.

That night the riders camped in an arroyo, a gully cut by the winter floods, below the level of the plain they were crossing. Young Charles cooked the meal over a fire of tiny dry sticks, and hardly a wisp of smoke rose to betray their camping place.

The moon came up and the night was warm. The fire died to embers. The men got ready to roll in their blankets and sleep. But before they did so, one man drew another aside.

"Satisfied, Majors?"

---

bandits—*thieves with guns*
convoying—*escorting; leading along*

undertook—*agreed to do*
arroyo (ə·roi′ō)

"More than satisfied!" Mr. Majors said with emphasis. "I heard it said that he was the toughest and the keenest plainsman around here. The way he got us out of that scrape yesterday and avoided trouble today has me convinced. Yes, Charles is our man if we can get him."

At the end of the journey Mr. Majors talked to Charles.

"Do you know how letters travel from New York to San Francisco, Charles?" he asked.

"I've never had occasion to send a letter anywhere," answered Charles. "There's not much letter-writing in these parts."

"Well," said Mr. Majors, "there are plenty of letters going from one part of our country to the other. The trouble is the time that's needed. It takes weeks and months to get a letter from the East Coast to the West."

"You can cover considerable ground on horseback in a month," said Charles thoughtfully.

"The letters don't go by horseback. They travel by ship to Panama, then overland to the West Coast. Then up the coast by ship. I've an idea that it can be done faster than that, and I want you to help me, Charles."

Charles listened while Mr. Majors explained his plan. (In those days there was train service from New York to St. Joseph, Missouri, but no farther west.)

"From St. Joseph on, I want relays of the toughest, the keenest, and bravest young men I can find," Mr. Majors said. "They will have short stages and the finest horses we can get. They will need to ride in winter and summer, through sun and storm, night and day."

148

Charles's eyes brightened. The idea sounded interesting. There might be some fine adventures riding like that.

"Nothing must interfere with the mail," said Mr. Majors. "It must go through so fast that in ten days a letter will be in San Francisco."

"Ten days' riding?"

"No. Ten days from New York to San Francisco, train and all."

"You must have worked out a plan," suggested Charles thoughtfully.

"We have. We are going to set up 198 stations from St. Joseph to San Francisco. We'll need five hundred of the best, speediest, and most enduring horses that we can find—and eighty riders." He paused and looked at Charles. "It will take more than pluck," he said. "Carrying the mail is an important business. It's a responsibility. The young men must be able to keep clear of trouble—no drinking, no fighting, no gambling or quarreling. And they must be honest and faithful."

Charles was looking more and more interested.

"It's a dangerous job, Charles. Interested?"

"Might be," said Charles briefly.

Mr. Majors brought out a rough map. "We're picking only the best men. I'd want you to help pick the men for this part of the country and have charge of them. And your own ride would be from here to here." He pointed out a section on the map.

"Not so long a ride!" said Charles.

"But it's a bad stretch in the winter." Mr. Majors was watching Charles quietly. "Here's the point. Rain or storm, snow or sleet, blizzard or drought, war or peace, Indians or highwaymen, the mail must go through! The man before you is due at your station a certain time. You must be saddled and mounted at that time. When he arrives there must be no delay in transferring the mail pouch. It will be done before his horse stops. You will go on at all speed to the next station. Yours will be a night ride."

Young Charles smiled a slow smile. He could imagine that race through the night. Dangerous, yes, but exciting.

"There's one other thing," said Mr. Majors. "Our outfit is going to have the finest horses and the best horsemen. We must have men who are of fine character. We are choosing only men who are willing to sign this pledge." He laid on the table before the young man a statement, written in a clear, plain hand. "Read it," he said, "and read it carefully."

Charles read: "I do hereby swear before the great and living God that during my engagement and while I am an employee of Russell, Majors, and Waddell, I will under no circumstances use profane language; that I will drink no intoxicating liquors; that I will not quarrel or fight with other employees of the firm; and that in every respect I will conduct myself honestly, be faithful to my duties, and so direct all my acts as to win the confidence of my employers. So help me God."

It was a stiff pledge. Most of the horsemen of that wild western country did freely all those things that were forbidden in the pledge.

"The mail's a responsibility," Mr. Majors went on slowly. "We can't risk having weak men. And besides, we want our riders to act in a godly way."

Young Charles thought it over. "I'll make the pledge," he said. "It's not asking too much."

Mr. Majors' eyes shone with pleasure. He looked with satisfaction at the long, lean figure before him. He didn't need to be told that Charles would be equal to anything that might come up. "Wish I could be as sure of all of them as I am of this man," he thought to himself.

Young Charles signed the pledge. Mr. Majors pulled from his saddlebags a small leather-bound Bible. "We don't ask any pledge about reading the Bible, Charles," he said. "That's any man's own affair. But carry this little Book with you and read it. Reading the Book will make it easier to keep the pledge you have signed."

Over and over again Mr. Majors talked to one man and another. At last all had been selected. Each one had signed the pledge. Each one had his little leather-bound Bible and his trusty horses.

The day of April 3, 1860 arrived. A great crowd awaited at the railway station at St. Joseph, Missouri. The train came puffing in—late! With all haste the mail, in which that first day were forty-nine letters, five telegrams and some newspapers, was stuffed into the leather saddlebag that was to carry them, and the gaily dressed, high-booted, eagle-eyed young rider swung into his saddle and was off.

Darkness came. Still the rider sped on. Four times he changed horses. And then at the end of a stretch of seventy-five miles another rider swung into the trail beside him. As

they raced along together, the mail pouch was handed from the first man to the second. On and on and on! The thunder of hoofs was stilled only for the brief seconds when each rider swung from a tired horse to the one held waiting beside the trail. On and on and on!

So began the shuttle service of the Pony Express. Through sun and rain, through spring and winter, through calm and storm the men rode. Young Charles and the others never failed.

In the days between their wild rides carrying the mail, they lived according to their pledge, and many a one found comfort and help in the little leather-bound Book that went with him, in sunshine or storm, along the trail of the overland express.

Time to Think

1. How did Mr. Majors know that Charles would be a good worker for the Pony Express?

2. Why was the Pony Express needed?

3. Was Charles afraid when he heard that he would be riding at night?

4. Why was each rider required to sign the pledge?

5. Why did Mr. Majors think it was important for each rider to carry a Bible?

The Pony Rider

Howard R. Driggs

The mail's got to go through, boy—
    got to go through.
Do you sense what that means?
There'll be deserts to dare and rivers to swim,
And canyon defiles where Indians may lurk
To cut short your run with a flint-headed shaft;
And you can't stop to fight—
    You must ride, boy,
        Just ride like the wind.

Spare your horse?—yes and no;
Treat him square, boy, of course;
But the mail's got to go through,
    And it's up to the horse
    To carry it through
Though his heart thumps his side,
Get the best he can give;
If he drops on the trail,
    Just grab up the mail,
Get another and ride,
    Just ride like the wind.

Another thing—mark me—
    Let liquor alone.
You'll need all your brains
    To win this game;
And don't curse and swear;
You'd better keep God right close by your side,
Then you never can fail to bring through the mail.
I've your word. Here's my hand!
    Now ride, boy,
        Just ride like the wind.

---

flint—*a hard rock used to spark a fire*

The Soldier's Reprieve

Mrs. R. Robbins

Benjamin Owen was a young soldier for the North in the Civil War. One day a terrible message came to his parents—their Benjamin was to be shot for sleeping at his post. When the news spread through the Vermont farm village, Mr. Allen, the minister, came to comfort the family.

"I thought, Mr. Allen," said the sorrowing father, "when I gave my Bennie to his country, that not a father in all this broad land made so precious a gift,—no, not one. The dear boy only slept a minute—just one little minute—at his post. I know that was all, for Bennie never dozed over a duty. How prompt and trustworthy he was!

"I know he fell asleep only one little second. He was so young, and not strong, that boy of mine! Why, he was as tall as I, and only eighteen! And now they shoot him because he was found asleep when doing sentinel duty!

" 'I should be ashamed, Father,' Bennie said, 'when I was a man, to think I never used this great right arm'—and he held it out so proudly before me—'for my country, when it needed it.'

---

reprieve—*cancellation of punishment*   sentinel duty—*guard duty*

155

" 'Go, then, my boy!' I said, 'and God keep you!' God has kept him, I think, Mr. Allen;" and the farmer repeated those last words slowly, as if, in spite of his reason, his heart doubted them.

"Like the apple of his eye, Mr. Owen, doubt it not!"

Blossom, Bennie's sister, sat near them, listening with pale cheeks. Now she answered a gentle tap at the kitchen door, opening it to receive from a neighbor's hand a letter. "It is from him," was all she said.

It was like a message from the dead! Mr. Owen took the letter but could not break the envelope on account of his trembling fingers. He held it toward Mr. Allen, with the helplessness of a child.

The minister opened it and read as follows:

Dear Father,

When this reaches you, I shall be in eternity. At first, it seemed awful to me; but I have thought about it so much now that it has no terror. I thought, Father, that my death might have come on the battlefield, for my country, and that, when I fell, it would be fighting gloriously; but to be shot down like a dog for nearly betraying it—to die for neglect of duty! O Father, I wonder the very thought does not kill me! But I shall not disgrace you. I am going to write you all about it; and when I am gone, you may tell my comrades; I cannot now.

You know I promised Jemmie Carr's mother I would look after her boy, and when he fell sick, I did all I could for him. He was not strong when he was ordered back into the ranks, and the day before that night, I carried all his baggage, besides my own, on our march. Toward night we went in on double-quick, the fastest marching pace, and the baggage began to feel very heavy. Everybody was tired; and as for Jemmie, if I had not lent him an arm now and then, he would have dropped by the way.

I was tired out when we came into camp; and then it was Jemmie's turn to be sentry, and I would take his place; but I was too tired, Father. I could not have kept awake if a gun had been pointed at my head; but I did not know it until—well, until it was too late.

"God be thanked!" interrupted Mr. Owen, reverently. "I knew Bennie was not the boy to sleep carelessly."

---

sentry—*a guard placed in a certain spot to keep people from passing*

*They tell me today that I have a short reprieve—
given to me by circumstances—"time to write to you,"
our good Colonel says. Forgive him, Father; he only
does his duty. He would gladly save me if he could; and
do not lay my death up against Jemmie. The poor boy is
broken-hearted, and does nothing but beg and entreat
them to let him die in my stead.*

*I can't bear to think of Mother and Blossom. Comfort
them, Father! Tell them I die as a brave boy should, and
that, when the war is over, they will not be ashamed of
me, as they must be now. God help me; it is very hard
to bear! Goodbye, Father!*

*Tonight, in the early twilight, I shall see the cows all
coming home from pasture, and precious little Blossom
standing on the back stoop, waiting for me—but I shall
never, never come! God bless you all!*

Forgive your poor Bennie.

Late that night the door of the back stoop opened softly,
and a little figure glided out and down the footpath to the
road that led by the mill. She seemed rather flying than
walking, turning her head neither to the right nor the left,
looking only now and then to Heaven, and folding her hands,
as if in prayer.

Two hours later, the same young girl stood at Mill Depot,
watching the coming of the night train; and the conductor, as
he reached down to lift her into the car, wondered at the tear-
stained face that was upturned toward the dim lantern he

158

held in his hand. A few questions and ready answers told him all; and no father could have cared more tenderly for his only child than he did for Blossom.

She was on her way to Washington to ask President Lincoln for her brother's life. She had stolen away, leaving only a note to tell her father where and why she had gone. She had taken Bennie's letter with her. No good, kind heart like the President's could refuse to be melted by it. The next morning they reached New York, and the conductor hurried her on to Washington. Every minute, now, might be the means of saving her brother's life. And so, in an incredibly short time, Blossom reached the capital, and hastened immediately to the White House.

The President had but just seated himself at his morning's task of looking over and signing important papers, when, without one word of announcement, the door softly opened, and Blossom, with downcast eyes and folded hands, stood before him.

"Well, my child," he said, in his pleasant, cheerful tones, "what do you want so bright and early in the morning?"

"Bennie's life, please, sir," faltered Blossom.

"Bennie? Who is Bennie?"

"My brother, sir. They are going to shoot him for sleeping at his post."

"O yes," and Mr. Lincoln ran his eye over the papers before him. "I remember! It was a fatal sleep. You see, child, it was at a time of special danger. Thousands of lives might have been lost through his negligence."

"So my father said," replied Blossom, gravely; "but poor Bennie was so tired, sir, and Jemmie so weak. He did the

159

work of two, sir, and it was Jemmie's night, not his; but Jemmie was too tired, and Bennie never thought about himself—that he was tired, too."

"What is this you say, child? Come here; I do not understand," and the kind man caught eagerly, as ever, at something to justify the offense.

Blossom went to him. He put his hand tenderly on her shoulder and turned up the pale, anxious face toward his. How tall he seemed, and he was President of the United States, too! A dim thought of this kind passed through Blossom's mind; but she told her simple and straightforward story and handed Mr. Lincoln Bennie's letter to read.

He read it carefully; then, taking up his pen, he wrote a few hasty lines and rang his bell.

Blossom heard this order given: "Send this dispatch at once."

The President turned to the girl and said, "Go home, my child, and tell that father of yours that Abraham Lincoln thinks the life of his son far too precious to be lost. Go back, or—wait until tomorrow; Bennie will need a change after he has so bravely faced death; he shall go with you."

"God bless you, sir," said Blossom; and who shall doubt that God heard and registered the request?

Two days after this interview, the young soldier came to the White House with his little sister. He was called into the President's private room, and a badge of promotion to lieutenant was fastened upon his shoulder. Mr. Lincoln then said, "The soldier that could carry a sick comrade's baggage and die for the act without complaining deserves well of his country."

Then Bennie and Blossom took their way to their Green Mountain home. A crowd gathered at the Mill Depot to welcome them back; and as farmer Owen's hand grasped that of his boy, tears flowed down his cheeks, and he was heard to say fervently, "The Lord be praised."

Time to Think

1. Why did Bennie fall asleep at his post?
2. How could Bennie's father be sure that he had only slept a minute?
3. Was Bennie angry with the men who sentenced him to death?
4. Who was responsible for saving Bennie's life?
5. Why was Bennie honored by President Lincoln?

Journey to America

The Story of a Family from Dalmatia
Clara Ingram Judson

Dalmatia is a region of Croatia, a country of
Eastern Europe. At the time this story takes place, it
was not a part of Croatia, but most of its people were
Croatians. Like people in lands all over the world, the
Petrovich family dreamed of going to America.

Petar Petrovich hurried back from the post office, panting
from the run but with his face a happy glow. "You have a
letter, Mama!" he shouted. "A fat letter."

"A letter!" Mama grabbed it, clutched it to her heart.
Anka, the youngest sister, dropped the cabbage she was

Dalmatia (dăl·mā′shə)   **Petrovich** (pĕt′rō·vĭch)   **Anka** (äng′kə)
Croatia (krō·ā′shə)   **Petar** (pē′tär)

162

slicing. Nona, the grandmother, stopped milking the goat, and Yovan, the brother, ran from under the olive tree where he had been playing.

"Is it from Papa?" Yovan asked. Papa had gone to America nearly two years ago, in 1904, and had been trying to earn enough money to send for Mama and the children.

"From your Papa," Mama said proudly. "Wait now." She slit the envelope and spread the contents on her lap.

"It has many papers," Yovan said. This was different from the other letters. Mama read, silently. When she put the letter down, her eyes glistened.

"Your Papa says, 'Come as soon as you can. There is work for all. I have bought us a house. America is a good place.'"

Nona (nō'nə)   Yovan (yō·vŏn')

"We are to go to America *now?*" Petar thought he had not heard rightly.

"You heard the letter," Mama said. "Wait, this other paper tells what I am to do."

"His brother, Josip, is to go with me to Split to see about passage. Here are tickets for Petar," Mama checked each one, "Anka, Yovan, Mama—"

"Where is Nona's?" asked Anka quickly.

Mama searched through the papers nervously and came upon a small sheet with Papa's writing. "There is not enough money for Nona this time," she read, "But when we are all working, we will send for her."

"We cannot go without Nona," Yovan said.

They looked at each other in misery. Leave Nona? She would have to go to live on the cousin's cherry farm.

"Your papa does the best he can," Mama said loyally.

But the surprise was spoiled. What would they have done without Nona while Papa was away? They couldn't leave her.

"The box under the bed," Petar shouted. "How could we forget!" He was in the house, on his knees, pulling at the chest.

"What good will that do?" Mama cried. "A few dinars! That will not take Nona to America."

"Look, Mama! When have you counted these? Did you know we had so many?" Petar had yanked open the box, dumped the coins on the stone floor, where they rolled this way and that in confusion. Anka and Yovan ran to gather them while Petar began to count and set them in piles, like a banker.

Josip (yô'sēp)   **dinars** (dĭ·närz')—*coins*

164

Round-eyed, they watched him silently. They had not guessed that one dinar after another, each dropped in with sacrifice, would amount to so many in two years.

"Look in the letter, Mama," Petar paused to say. "See how much it takes for one person to go to America."

Mama looked but was too excited to read; she had to turn the paper over to Petar. Not a word was spoken while he read and then continued counting.

"Not enough," he said bleakly. He looked from one to the other for suggestions.

"Of course!" he shouted. "We shall sell the goat—"

"Sell our goat?" Yovan, the little six-year-old brother, was horrified. The goat was a member of the family.

"Yes," Petar repeated, hardening his heart. "Would you leave Nona behind? The postmaster will be glad to buy her; he is always saying we have a fine goat. The storekeeper's wife will buy the geese; she told me last week she would take them for groceries we needed. Maybe that will be enough. Or maybe we can sell something else." Petar ran an appraising eye over the room. Anka and Yovan were numb with amazement. Selling precious things—what would they do without them?

In half an hour the news had spread to the village, and friends filled the house and dooryard. Those Petrovichs, who had had such a hard time, going to America! Who would have thought? Petar had no trouble bargaining for the goat and geese, and cautious new owners took the creatures home. Neighbors bid for the loom and wheel; Josip bargained for the old bed.

The postmaster knelt by Petar and counted out the money. "I think you will have enough for Nona's ticket, Petar," he said quietly. "Tomorrow, go with your mama to Split and get the truth about the matter."

There was little sleep in the Petrovich cottage that night. The next day, Nona, Anka, and Yovan could hardly wait until afternoon when the others returned with news.

"Nona is to go!" Anka cried, seeing their happy faces.

"We sail for America on Tuesday," Petar said, "*all* of us."

"I will work hard to pay you," Nona said, when she had swallowed the lump in her throat. "And now, Yovan, stir the fire and let us eat the good food neighbors have brought."

The ship was to sail Tuesday, and this was Friday. Quilts and clothing must be washed, the house made clean. Fishhooks, needles, and spoons must be sorted. Each person was to carry a carpetbag, slung over his shoulder. In these Mama packed small articles and clothing. Quilts were folded and tied into a bundle which was Petar's responsibility.

Sunday was like a holiday with neighbors coming and going, people visiting and saying farewells after church. Everyone made much of the children, and Petar had never felt so important.

"As soon as I get to America, I shall get a job and earn a lot of money," he said to Yovan, as they walked home.

"I shall work, too," Yovan boasted, his head quite turned with all the talk. It didn't occur to either boy that the customs, the very language, would be different in America.

Tuesday, they sailed for Genoa and there took passage in the steerage of a ship bound for New York. Yovan was fright-

---

Genoa (jĕn′ō·ə)   steerage—*section of the ship that has the cheapest rooms*

166

ened by the huge ship. He thought it looked higher than a church. A small red gangplank like a tongue was thrust out from a hole, and across this, a long line of passengers boarded.

The Petrovich family had a cabin to themselves, with shelflike beds on either side. Meals, served in a crowded dining room, were bread and coffee, with stew once a day. Petar and Yovan roamed the part of the ship open to steerage passengers. But the women, shy of noise, strangers, and sounds of many languages, stayed in the cabin except for meals.

On the Atlantic, storms tossed the ship, and Anka was so sick she could not leave her bed. Their clothing was too light for such weather; Yovan was kept inside. Petar turned up his collar and sat in the lee of one of the great smokestacks where

---

lee—*the side protected from the wind*

the men gathered. Never had he seen so many strange people—Germans, Spaniards, French, Dutch, and Italians. Few spoke Croatian, the language of Dalmatia, and the other languages sounded like so much childish jabber. A Dalmatian going to New York on his second trip sat by him one day, and Petar exclaimed about the languages.

"You will find it a task to learn English," the man remarked.

"English?" Petar exclaimed. "My Papa is in America. In Biloxi, America. I am not going to England."

"But Americans speak English," the man said.

"That is funny." Petar was puzzled and doubting, even though the man said he had been in America. "Why?"

"Because it is their mother tongue."

Petar shook his head. That explained nothing to him.

"You speak Croatian, yet you do not live in Croatia."

"Everyone speaks Croatian," Petar said, "or Italian."

"Everyone you have known, maybe." The man grinned at Petar. The boy had much to learn, he knew from his own experience. "Dalmatia has been under many rulers—Turks, Venetians, French, Austrians, yet the people speak their mother tongue of Croatia. That is natural. And Americans speak English."

"Is this English hard to learn?" Petar asked. "My Papa did not write about English."

"Some find it very hard. But a man must learn it. If he does not, he will stay a greenhorn. You are only a boy; you can go to school and learn quickly."

He got up to go in, chilled with the cold, and Petar had no time to tell him that he would get a job and earn big money before he went to school.

One morning, six weeks from the day they sailed, the ship was astir early. Petar went out to investigate.

"We are coming into the harbor!" he exclaimed, running back to the cabin to tell the others. "In the night we have come to America. We must be on deck quickly, Mama!"

Soon the Petrovich family, bag and baggage, was huddled in a corner of the crowded steerage deck. Trunks, chests, bundles, and people were jammed together. Children cried with excitement and no breakfast, women looked sick and frightened with worry, while men blustered and shouted to hide their terror of this new land.

Venetians (və·nē′shənz)
greenhorn—*a newcomer*
astir—*full of motion*

As the ship swung around, silence fell on the crowd. A gleam of sunshine lighted a statue on an island in the harbor, showing a hand raised to hold a torch blazing in welcome, a face solemn in greeting. Tears glistened on faces that suddenly put aside fear. Mothers lifted children to see the statue; people shouted, wept, cheered.

"That is the Statue of Liberty," people whispered in a dozen languages.

"This is America, the land of the free."

Time to Think

1. How was Papa's good news that the family could go to America spoiled?
2. How did the family raise money for Nona's ticket?
3. Were the neighbors jealous that the Petrovichs could go to America? How do you know?
4. What did Petar want to do as soon as he arrived in America?
5. Why was Petar surprised to hear that he would have to learn English?
6. Why were the Petrovichs so happy to arrive in America, even when they realized they had a lot to learn?

America

Leone Harr

What is America?
The stark wild land of the Eskimo,
Of the northern lights and the midnight sun;
The storied wall of the Alamo
That echoed to freedom's thundering guns.
The Hudson's stately Palisades
And Plymouth Rock and the White House dome;
South to the Florida Everglades
Where the fountain of youth had its fabled home.
    That is America.

What is America?
The beckoning lure of the Oregon Trail . . .
Prairie schooners lumbering west,
Pony Express with the overland mail,
The forty-niners' treasure chest.
It's the steadfast faith at Valley Forge
Where freedom's roots struck deep to dwell.
It's the Colorado's awesome gorge . . .
It's the Painted Desert's magnetic spell.
    That is America.

Palisades—*a row of steep cliffs along the bank of the*
   Hudson River
gorge—*a deep passage with rock walls*

What is America?
It's the country known as the melting pot
Where Liberty's torch is held on high.
It's the Unknown Soldier's burial plot;
It's the evening star in the sunset sky.
It's the age-old calm of the towering peaks;
It's the scent of sage in the rain-swept air.
It's the call of the wilderness that speaks
To the venturesome few who its dangers dare.
        That is America.

What is America?
It's the reaching spire of the village church
That bears aloft our prayers to God.
It's the eagle's scream from his lofty perch;
It's the life that springs from the lowly sod.
It's your land and my land held in trust
For those who died on land and sea;
Keep it the same for them we must
In all its glorious traditions . . . for we
        Are Americans.

---

sage—*a fragrant plant whose leaves are used in cooking*
spire—*a structure that goes to a point at the top*

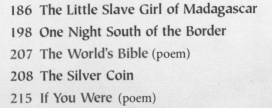

Missionary Call

UNIT
3

Missionary Call

Patricia Finrow Clark

We want to go to Heaven,
  But we cannot find the way.
Won't someone come to tell us,
  To teach us how to pray?

We want to go to Heaven,
  But which idol tells us true?
Oh, children of America,
  We're waiting now for you!

The Book from the Street

Alice Geer Kelsey

Of all the books in the world, none is so important for you to read as the one this story is about.

Kiku nearly stepped on the little book before she noticed it lying in the street of her small village in the hills of Japan. The book was dirty and crumpled. Others had been walking on it.

Like every Japanese schoolgirl, Kiku loved to read. Even a small and dirty book interested her. She stooped to pick it up. She walked toward home slowly, reading as she walked.

This little book was very different from her schoolbooks, or from the magazines she liked to buy when she had a few extra yen. She finished reading it before she spread her bed pad on the straw mats of the floor to sleep that night. She read parts of it over again the next day.

She thought of the little book when she heard her father and mother talking about a neighbor, Ayako-San.

"Poor Ayako-San!" sighed Kiku's mother. "She is lonely and sad ever since her husband died."

"She is looking everywhere for comfort," said Kiku's father. "She goes often to the Shinto shrine. She pays many yen for paper prayers at the shrine. She has been to the Buddhist priest also. Nothing he says helps her. She even made a pilgrimage to the sacred Temple city, but still she weeps and mourns."

"She should think of her children," said Kiku's mother. "She should think of making a happy home for them. There must be something to make her glad to live again."

Then Kiku had her idea. On her way to school that morning, Kiku stopped at the home of Ayako-San. As usual, she found the poor woman crying. Kiku held out the little book she had found in the street.

Kiku (kē·kōo)
yen—*a Japanese coin*
Ayako-San (ī·yä·kə·sän)

Shinto—*a Japanese religion*
pilgrimage—*a journey to visit a shrine*

"Take it and read it," said Kiku. "I found it in the street where someone had dropped it. I read it. There is a wonderful story in it of a man who helps those who are sad and helpless. I thought of you. I think you will like the story."

Ayako-San bowed her thanks. Even a very sad Japanese lady would remember to be polite.

Kiku ran toward school. Ayako-San wiped her eyes on the gray sleeve of her kimono. Now she could see the Japanese characters of the little torn book. She would read a few words just to see what Kiku thought was so wonderful.

Ayako-San read one page—and another—and another. It was just what Kiku had said, the "wonderful story of a man who helps those who are sad and helpless." She turned to what was left of the cover page and found the book was named *St. Luke's Gospel*.

As Ayako-San read the little book again and again, she found much that she could understand and much that she could not understand. She wished there was someone to tell her, but nobody in that hill village knew. Nobody could answer Ayako-San's questions.

One day she walked down the rough trails to the market town to sell the eggs her few hens had laid. Right in the center of the busy market she saw a man talking to a crowd. She joined them to hear what he was saying. He was talking about the man of her little book—Jesus Christ! When the man finished talking, there were still questions Ayako-San wanted to ask.

"Will you come to my village?" Ayako-San pointed toward the road leading into the hills. "Nobody there knows about Jesus. Will you come and tell us?"

kimono—*a loose robe worn by Japanese people*

Of course, the answer was "yes" from the seller of Bibles.

In a few months, there were enough Christians in that little village to make a church.

When they met, there was none with a face more full of calm and peace than Ayako-San. And there was none more full of excitement than Kiku. She knew that Jesus had brought new joy into her village because she had stooped to pick up the little book in the street—and had read it—and had shared it.

"Thou shalt find Him,
if thou seek Him with all thy heart."
—*Deuteronomy 4:29*

Time to Think _____

1. What book did Kiku find in the street?
2. Why did Kiku give the Book to Ayako-San?
3. Who helped Ayako-San understand what she read in the Book?
4. What happened as a result of Kiku finding the Book and sharing it?
5. Why was the Book from the street important even though it was old and torn?

My Old Bible

Author Unknown

Though the cover is worn,
And the pages are torn,
And though places bear traces of tears,
Yet more precious than gold
Is this Book worn and old,
That can shatter and scatter my fears.

This old Book is my guide,
'Tis a friend by my side,
It will lighten and brighten my way;
And each promise I find
Soothes and gladdens the mind,
As I read it and heed it each day.

To this Book I will cling,
Of its worth I will sing,
Tho' great losses and crosses be mine;
For I cannot despair,
Though surrounded by care,
While possessing this blessing divine.

---

heed—*pay attention to*

181

David Livingstone:
Learning to Work for God

Dora C. Abdy (adapted)

During the 1800s, people from many nations eagerly read newspaper accounts of David Livingstone's explorations of Africa. Year after year, this famous Christian braved dangers from tropical diseases, hostile slave traders, and wild beasts, always refusing to give up, even after being mauled by a lion. His goal in life was to win Africans to Christ and to open pathways for other missionaries to follow. How did he become a person of such great determination and courage?

In an ordinary house in the poor part of Blantyre, Scotland, there was born in 1813 a blue-eyed baby boy who became famous throughout the world as David Livingstone, the great missionary-explorer of Africa. Though the house was small, those who lived in it had great character.

Blantyre (blăn′tīr)

Neil Livingstone, David's father, was a traveling tea sales-
man, but he was more interested in selling Bibles and giving
gospel tracts to his customers than in gaining large profits.
He was also a Sunday school teacher and an ardent member
of a missionary society. He taught his seven children to be as
keen and persevering as he was himself. He would never let
his boys be rude or ungenerous. He used to remind them
that they came of a freeborn Highland family, and that
though they were poor, not one of the family had ever been
known to be dishonest.

David's mother was always bright and serene and in good
spirits, and she used to tell her children the most lovely
stories. As a child, David showed, both in play and in work,
the courage and perseverance and calmness that he had
received from his father and mother. When he was a lad of
nine, David stood before his father and recited the whole of
Psalm 119 with only five mistakes. This longest chapter in
the Bible has 176 verses, almost all about God's Word.

David was equally persevering in his work. When he was
only ten years old, he went to work at the village cotton mill.
He began work at six in the morning and did not go home
until eight in the evening. He soon found that his work
would not need much brain power, for it only meant watching the whirling spools of cotton and joining together any
thread that happened to snap. With his first week's wages he
bought a Latin book, and he gave the rest of the money to his
mother. In those days, Latin was the language everyone who
wanted to learn much needed to be able to read. The next

---

ardent—*full of strong feeling or devotion*
serene—*still and quiet*

week he propped up his Latin book on the end of the spinning jenny, and as he walked up and down, he learned a few words at a time. As he learned his Latin in this way, he was also learning to concentrate in the midst of noise and activity. This skill would greatly help him in the jungles of Africa.

When he got home at night, he was soon deep in his books again, and he would have gone on till past midnight if his mother had not come in and blown out his candle. By the time he was sixteen, he knew the great Latin writers well and had read all he could lay his hands on. He especially

spinning jenny—*a machine used to spin thread*

enjoyed reading science books, because they helped him understand the greatness and wisdom of God.

David left his home at the age of eighteen to study to be a doctor. He would study for six months, go home to earn more money for school, and then return to school. Then, hearing about a medical missionary in China, he felt God calling him to be a missionary doctor. After meeting Dr. Robert Moffat, a pioneer missionary to Africa, he knew that he, too, would be a missionary to Africa. He studied and trained some more and then followed God's call as a pioneer missionary to the parts of Africa where no Christian had ever been before. He explored deep into the heart of Africa, opening trails for other missionaries to follow, and he used every opportunity to tell his African friends about salvation through Christ.

Time to Think

1. Who taught David to be honest and to work hard?
2. What did David do at age nine that proved he knew how to persevere?
3. Why did David take his Latin book to work with him?
4. How did learning Latin at work prepare David for his future ministry?
5. After reading this story, what things do you think were important to David Livingstone throughout his life?

The Little Slave Girl of Madagascar

Grace W. McGarvan

Madagascar (1882)
Madagascar, the world's fourth-largest island, lies off
the eastern coast of Africa. For many centuries, the people
of Madagascar and other parts of Africa lived in fear of
being captured by slave raiders or tribal warriors and sold
as slaves to members of other tribes. This is the true story
of one such captive who knew the secret to true freedom
and who gladly shared it with those around her.

Birdling, the newly captured slave child, was quivering all
over with sobs. She tried hard to control herself, for the slave
master was looking angrily in her direction. Finally he came
and stood over her, whip in hand.

"Have done with weeping," he commanded sternly.
"Would you have me lash you?"

Birdling stopped crying and looked at him in utter horror.
"Lash me?" she almost whispered. "You wouldn't!"

"And why not?" he answered roughly. "No longer are you
the pampered pet of some foolish mother. You are nothing
but a slave. In your home village, who cared what happened
to slaves?"

He strode away with a final warning. "The weeping is to
stop. How shall I sell you tomorrow if your face is all swollen
with tears?"

He had startled Birdling into stopping her tears. Fear of a whipping forced her to control her sobs.

What he had said was true. She knew it. All too true. No one in Madagascar cared what happened to slaves, not even in her own home village, now far, far away in the south. If the slaves bothered their owner, they were made to suffer for it. Certainly crying and sobbing would have received stern punishment.

Birdling made herself think of things other than home. She began to look around her. She pushed the sights and sounds of this new town between her and the memory of the laughter-filled happy home from which the slave raiders had snatched her. Her mother had been away making a visit in the next village, and her father had been out hunting in the moun-tains when she and others of the village had been captured. So she had hope that her parents were safe. She dared not think of their grief when they came gaily home and found her gone. They would miss their Birdling, as they had always called her, but they would know that a pretty child such as she was would perhaps be sold into a good home.

Birdling's tears soon dried. Once she began to look around her, she became interested in what was going on. She ate the sweet fruit that was brought her, although she did not know its name. She watched people go by, some in fine, rich clothes, attended by slaves. She wondered whether when morning came she would be following the litter in which some rich woman was carried by big, full-muscled slaves. She wondered whether she would be going through the noisy streets among the jostling crowds to a new home.

Morning came, and Birdling, as she waked to strange surroundings, nearly wept again. But the bustle around her caught her attention, and she was soon part of it all. The newly captured slaves were being made ready for sale.

Birdling was given a simple garment, and her hair was arranged in childlike style. Not for nothing had the keeper of slaves spent her life in making little new slave girls attractive to would-be purchasers.

Then came a time of waiting. The rich did not arrive too early at the market. Others came and bought some of the lower-priced slaves. Once in a while someone would ask the price of Birdling, looking at her as she sat, half-fearful, half-expectant, in the shade of a huge, flowering tree, with the other slaves grouped nearby.

But such ones always turned away on hearing the price that was being asked for her, although one or two said under the breath, "A beautiful child. They'll get what they're asking for her."

---

litter—*a seat mounted on poles carried by servants*

The sun still had not climbed high above the eastern horizon when a handsome litter arrived, carried by four slaves. A fifth carried a shade over the richly dressed young woman who rode in it. The slave master sprang to his feet. The lady in the litter must have some special need to have come herself and so early in the day. Of course it was wise to come early so that one might have the pick of the day's offerings. But often a trusted slave or an elderly relative was sent to make the choice.

"It is a house girl that I need," the young lady remarked, leaning over the side of the litter. The bearers held it aloft, standing quietly while their mistress let her eyes rove over the group of dejected captives. Their sorrow did not trouble her. It hardly occurred to her that slaves might have hearts and be sad. Slaves were something she had been used to all her life, and she regarded the feelings of a slave as she would those of a favorite dog. She knew that some of the slaves she was looking at had very likely been torn from their homes and families, but that was the usual way of securing servants when the supply was low.

One captive was not looking sad. It was Birdling. She was so interested in the appearance of the rich young lady and her litter that she was examining her with eager curiosity. No such person as she had ever entered Birdling's simple home!

"That girl there!" The young lady pointed to Birdling. "She looks intelligent. And she is attractive. Let her stand forth."

---

aloft—*up in the air*
rove—*to move about freely*

Before Birdling knew what was happening, the sale had been made and she had become the property of the rich young lady. Soon the litter was being borne swiftly through the gathering crowd. Birdling was trotting along behind, breathing hard as she tried to keep up to the quick steps of the trained litter bearers. A huge slave strode along beside her to make sure that she made no attempt to escape. He chuckled to himself at the hop, skip, and jump with which the new little slave moved.

Birdling was too young to have many duties, and she learned those she was given with a quickness that surprised and pleased her new mistress. It pleased her, too, that the child did not cry and fret.

"Were you born in slavery, Birdling?" she asked her care-lessly one day.

For a moment Birdling's eyes were flooded with tears. Then she stood up as straight as she could, blinked back the tears and answered quietly, "No, Mistress. My home was in the south. It was from there that the raiders snatched me. My parents did not even know."

Her mistress' face clouded. "Ah! I had not guessed. And you so very young! You keep so cheerful, Birdling mine. I would never have guessed." Then she frowned. "Never before have I had any slaves that were born free. I do not like to think that one of my slaves was once free. Better never to have tasted freedom than to lose it. But at least you are as well off with me as a slave child may be?" She made the last statement into a question.

Birdling smiled. "Mistress, you have made me happy and contented," she answered truthfully.

Just the same there were times when Birdling was lonely— lonely with a loneliness that began at her toes and crept through her to her fingertips. She would slip away then, if no one was needing her help, down to the bottom of the garden slope. Under the big trees there she would sit down. Pulling a book from her garment, where she carried it, she would read.

The book was one that she had been reading at the mo-ment that the slave raiders swooped down into the village. Without even thinking, she had clung to it when they carried her away and she had been allowed to keep it. It was her only book—the New Testament in the language of Madagascar.

No one in the household where she now lived was a Christian. But all the other slaves were amused at the sight of the pretty little slave girl sitting under the big trees at the foot of the garden slope. They used to creep down to look and to listen to her, reading, as the custom was, out loud. None of them could read. Not even their mistress could read. Only the educated slave who was overseer of the slaves and of the household could make sense out of the [strange] black and white marks in books.

All the household soon knew about Birdling's book, and that she could read it. But no one told the mistress.

"Who knows?" they said. "Our mistress is gentle and kind. But if it should offend her that a slave girl knows how to read, she might punish her, or forbid her to use her book, or even take it from her." So they kept the book a secret.

One hot summer afternoon Birdling's mistress wandered out into the garden in search of a breeze. She went down the slope where she had seldom been. As she walked she heard a low voice speaking but saw no one. Out of curiosity she followed the sound. There, at the foot of the slope, curled up on the gnarled root of a huge tree, she found Birdling, earnestly reading.

"What is this? Is it reciting a story you are, Birdling?"

Birdling stood up respectfully. She hid the small book behind her at first, then drew it forward. "No, Mistress, I was reading in my Holy Book."

"Reading? Can you read, Birdling?"

"Yes, Mistress. My father taught me."

Other slaves were standing uneasily in the background by then. Would the mistress be angry? Or would she be amused? To their astonishment, she was neither.

"Do you think you could teach me to read, Birdling?"

"Oh, yes, Mistress. It is not hard." The slave girl's eyes lit up with happiness. "With joy I would teach you."

Lessons began, and the New Testament was the textbook. There was no other book from which to learn.

Birdling started with some of the stories that Jesus told. She helped her mistress to learn how to read one story after another.

"But this is interesting!" cried the mistress. "These stories are wonderful!"

Birdling had to explain what some of the stories were meant to teach. Then her mistress wanted to know who the storyteller was. "Who was this Jesus?" she asked.

So the next reading lesson was from the Gospel of Luke. The little slave girl helped her mistress to begin reading the story of the starry night when Jesus was born. They read of how the angels sang as the glory of heaven shone down on earth and the Baby cradled in the manger.

The reading lesson came to an end early that day. "It takes too long. Read me the rest of the story," demanded the mistress. So Birdling read, while Mistress and older slaves listened enthralled to a story they had never heard before.

_____

enthralled—*completely attentive*

The mistress loved the stories. No lesson went by without reading a story. But Birdling did not pass by the teachings, nor the words of Jesus about himself, nor the events of history that followed the day of Pentecost.

"Come over when the sun is low," the mistress would send a message to her friends. "I have a new slave—a mere child. She can read! From a book she reads. And the book has in it the strangest and most winning stories and teachings I have ever heard. Come over and hear my Birdling read."

Perhaps the mistress wanted her friends to discover that she herself had learned to read! For she always took the book from Birdling's hands and opened it to this place and to that place. She would read slowly and clearly, to the surprise and envy of her friends.

"Birdling," said her mistress one day, "put aside the book and talk to me instead. Tell me how to become a follower of Jesus."

It was nothing surprising to Birdling that her mistress should want to become a Christian. How could one help but want to follow Jesus? How could one help but worship God, who loved earth people so much that he sent Jesus to be their Lord and Saviour?

But oh, how surprised Birdling was when, one day later on, her mistress called all her slaves before her! "You all know," she said very slowly, "that I am become a follower of Jesus. And being so, I cannot hold any child of God my slave."

And with that she freed them all and had no longer any slaves.

What a day of joy that was! The slaves could hardly believe their ears. To be freed! To belong no longer to anyone, but each to own his own self! To ask no man or woman whether one might come or go, but like the breeze to wander wherever one's desire led one! The slaves were overcome with joy.

Some sped to homes almost forgotten. Others stayed with the mistress and worked for wages, loyally and faithfully, as before they had worked from necessity.

Birdling went back to her father's home. She entered the house almost as one risen from the dead and brought with her happiness more than could be measured. Then she returned to live with and care for the mistress she had come to love.

One long journey they took, the two of them, and a band of helpers traveled with them. They went to where there were missionaries. They begged that the church send missionaries to their town in Madagascar to teach and to lead the new Christians in the Christian way. And in answer to that plea missionaries did come from a faraway land. But Madagascar and its climate were strange to them. Disease seized them, and one by one they died. So again, there was no one to lead and to teach the new followers of Jesus.

Yet the mistress was not discouraged. With the Bible in her hands she read and prayed and listened to the thoughts that God gave her. And with quiet persistence she taught everyone who was willing to learn from her.

Gradually there grew up in her town on the lovely island of Madagascar, so big an island that it is a country all of itself, a church with many, many members.

"And all because a lonely little slave girl read aloud from her New Testament," the Christians of that town will tell you proudly. "And because the heart of a rich young woman was open to the teachings of the Word of God to accept them and to live her life by them."

"My Word . . . shall not return unto Me void,
but it shall accomplish that which I please,
and it shall prosper in the thing
whereto I sent it."
—Isaiah 55:11

Time to Think _____

1. What made the rich lady notice Birdling?
2. What did Birdling do when she was feeling lonely?
3. Why were the other slaves so fascinated when Birdling read aloud?
4. Why did the other slaves keep Birdling's ability to read a secret?
5. How did the mistress learn about Jesus?
6. How was Birdling rewarded for the suffering she had endured?

One Night
South of the Border

Dorothy A. Stevens

Pablo turned the corner and walked rapidly toward the church. He hurriedly finished the roll of tortillas and beans he was eating. "Um-good," he murmured to himself.

Juan was waiting for him at the entrance to the church. He was nervous.

Pablo (pä′blō)   **Juan** (hwän)

"The seats are filling up. Am I glad you're here! There is talk of fight."

"Yes, I know," said Pablo. He had an air of confidence. His black eyes flashed. He'd never run away from a fight yet, and he certainly wouldn't now when Pastor Dominguez, Juan's father, was in danger.

"I'm glad the general missionary is here," Juan said. "He's met things like this before. Sometimes I think my dad is too kind."

It was a little after sundown, and the air was still hot, but it was getting cooler. Pablo could see that his friend Juan was a little volcano inside. He loved Jesus, and he loved his father, but he didn't want his father to get hurt, or be killed.

Pablo put his arm around his shoulders. "Juan, my friend, you needn't worry. As the song goes, 'God Will Take Care of You.' And He'll take care of your dad, too. Why, Benito, the Communist leader, might even become a Christian. Let's go inside."

They sat in some of the side seats near the front where they could see the congregation. The church seated about two hundred people, and was soon filled. The general missionary and Juan's father sat on the raised platform in front. Pablo watched the choir gather around the platform and press in so close they could hardly get their breath for singing. Small children had been parked on the edge of the platform when the mothers arrived and were now peacefully sleeping, in spite of the chatter of the crowd. Many people had walked

---

Dominguez (dō·mēng′gĕz)
general missionary—*a representative who travels from church to church*
Benito (bā·nēt′ō)

miles over the mountains, and some had come from the small town nearby to attend the church service.

Pablo could feel the sense of joyful expectation on the part of the congregation. But he also knew that deep down there was a sense of fear, too. For days, Benito and his Communist gang had advertised that they were going to break up the meeting and shame the God of the Christians.

Perhaps at this very moment, the gang was gathering on some side street, or in some saloon, and in a little while they would be coming with their sticks and stones to pick a fight and spoil the meeting.

Pablo noticed Juan's father whisper quietly to the general missionary and then step forward to the edge of the platform.

"This meeting," he said, "is opened in the name of Jesus Christ." His voice rang out with great assurance. Pablo noticed in the corners where the lamplight left flickering pools of shadow, that the late-comers suddenly sat erect, and behind them the entire congregation of more than two hundred eager faces drew in their breath as one person and waited for the long-expected service to fulfill their dreams.

After a brief prayer, the song leader blew a tone on his pitch pipe. The choir began to sing, and as the familiar words rang out, the congregation took up the tune and sang the words from memory. Pablo was deeply moved as he, too, sang:

> On a hill far away stood an old rugged cross,
> The emblem of suffering and shame;
> And I love that old cross where the dearest and best
> For a world of lost sinners was slain.

---

erect—*straight up*

Pablo knew that not many of the people could read, and in the dimness none of them could see the print, anyhow. But the sounds poured out into the garden, where now the crowd was so thick there was not room to put one foot in front of another.

Then Pablo heard in the distance the sound of marching feet. So it was true! Benito and his Communist gang were on their way to the church to break up the meeting, or even worse, to take Pastor Dominguez, Juan's father, out to beat him up or perhaps kill him. Nearer they came and nearer. Pablo could hear the shuffling feet of the crowd outside the church, and then the flickering light of the torches shone through the windows, and he knew that Benito's gang had arrived.

The group inside the church sang on. A shuffling noise in the back made Pablo realize that Benito was pushing through the crowd who were packed in the door of the church. He finally got through and sat down near the back. Pablo watched him. He could see hate and malice and envy written in every line of his face. What had he come to do? Would he stop the service? Would his gang outside begin to stone the crowd of interested worshipers and break the windows? And then would they take Juan's father and the general missionary and beat them? Pablo's courage had a battle with his fear, and he wasn't sure which won.

Suddenly he knew the singing had stopped, and he heard Pastor Dominguez reading:

God is our refuge and strength, a very present help in trouble. Therefore will not we fear, though the earth be

---

malice—*anger*

removed, and though the mountains be carried into the midst of the sea; Though the waters thereof roar and be troubled, though the mountains shake with the swelling thereof. Be still, and know that I am God: I will be exalted among the heathen, I will be exalted in the earth. The Lord of hosts is with us; the God of Jacob is our refuge. —*Ps. 46:1–3, 10–11*

Could it be, thought Pablo, that God would be exalted among the heathen Communists? Did that mean Benito and his gang?

He heard the pastor say: "Mr. Choirmaster, lead us in the song, 'I Would Be True,' please."

The young people knew this well, and they sang with enthusiasm. Pablo watched Benito. He seemed to be enjoying the singing. His face had lost a little of its hate.

After the song, Pastor Dominguez called for a period of prayer. He asked anyone who felt led of God's Spirit to pray. The prayers began. Down deep, Pablo felt a desire to pray, but he didn't know just how to express his feeling. He wanted to

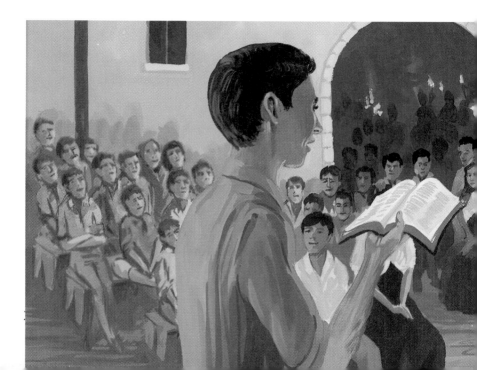

pray that God would make Benito realize he was a sinner and turn to God for forgiveness. The prayers were brief and came quickly one after another. Juan prayed. And so Pablo prayed, too. "O God, make us know how big sinners we are and save us from our sins."

Now the choir was singing again, and a sort of peace settled down on the congregation. Pablo knew that the general missionary soon would be speaking, and he wondered how he felt. What would he say? He saw from the earnest look upon his face that he realized what a great opportunity was his—to speak tonight to the Communist leader in the community. If only he could be won to Christ! Benito was a leader among the youth of the city.

The general missionary stepped forward and began to speak:

"I have heard your pastor open the meeting in the name of Jesus Christ. I have just read on the side of this table that faces us these words: 'Sir, we would see Jesus.' Let us look at

Him, love Him, serve Him, from this night on forever."
Pablo heard him go on to tell how wicked man was, how
God in His love had sent Jesus to save sinful man from his
sins, how the forgiveness of God was available for any who
turned to Him with truly repentant hearts. It was easy to see
that the missionary was not afraid.

Pablo looked at Benito. He seemed to be impressed.
Drops of sweat appeared on his face as if he was deeply
moved.

The voice of the general missionary rang out until it
reached the hearers in the garden around the church.
Benito's men out there were no doubt hearing the message,
too. Pablo wondered what they thought. Were they wondering why their leader, who was inside, did not act, as he had
said he would? Pablo's glance went from the speaker to the
pastor to Benito and back again. Surely God is moving here,
thought Pablo. The pastor was in prayer. The missionary
was speaking with great power. And it looked like Benito
was being convicted of his sins.

It was a long sermon. After an hour, the missionary
concluded his message with a brief prayer: "Please, God," he
said, "touch the hearts of the unbelievers. Bring to them
faith and joy such as we have."

The congregation breathed a powerful "Amen" and
waited expectantly. The invitation was given as a hymn was
sung.

"Who will accept this great salvation, this gift of God
through Jesus Christ?" Pablo joyfully watched a number of
boys and girls begin to push their way toward the front. He
was glad he was a Christian. There was a stirring among the

older people. The crowd was great, and people would find it difficult to push their way through to the front. Pablo heard the general missionary say:

"If you can't get down here to the front, stand where you are and lift your hands. We can see you. Someone will come to you."

Pablo wondered. Would this be the time the Communist visitors would begin to break up the meeting?

Pablo saw the Communist leader push his way to the front and stand up on the first bench.

"Hear me," he said. Ah, the time had come! Now they were going to hear a denial of the sermon. Soon the Communist thugs would break up the meeting. Maybe not! The face of the Communist leader seemed softer than ever before. He went on.

"My friends, I came here with a trained band of companions to break up this meeting, and to force you to listen to the good news of Communism, so that for once you could have the truth. My friends are waiting outside for a word from me to start making trouble."

"Boys," Benito called in a loud voice, and the congregation was stunned. "Boys, cast away your rocks! Do not throw them! We have heard the truth tonight. We did not bring it. If I am still your leader, with all the strength that is in me, I urge you to join me and follow the living God of whom this missionary has spoken."

Pablo listened as Benito spoke to the congregation, and he heard him say:

"I, who boasted the power to overcome you in the name of Communism, beg of you to receive me as a sinner who has found his Savior, the living Christ. I want what you have—faith, joy, and courage."

Pablo's heart was overflowing with gratitude. Now Juan and Pastor Dominguez would be safe, and many people would turn to Christ. The Communists had lost their leader; many of them would let Benito guide them into the new movement under the leadership of Jesus Christ.

The meeting was over in a moment with the spontaneous singing of the doxology on the part of the congregation. Pablo shouted with his lips and prayed with his heart:

"Praise God from whom all blessings flow. . . ."

---

spontaneous—*not planned*
doxology—*a short hymn of praise*

Time to Think

1. What was Juan afraid would happen?
2. Why did Juan fear for his father's safety?
3. What happened when Benito and his men arrived at the meeting?
4. What did Benito think of the service?
5. What announcement did he make at the end?
6. How did Pablo feel when the meeting was over?

The World's Bible

Annie Johnson Flint

Christ has no hands but our hands
    To do His work today;
He has no feet but our feet
    To lead men in His way;
He has no tongue but our tongue
    To tell men how He died;
He has no help but our help
    To bring them to His side.

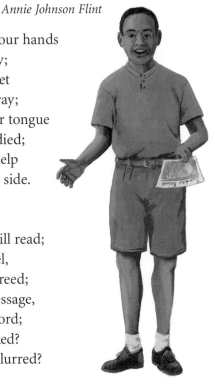

We are the only Bible
    The careless world will read;
We are the sinner's gospel,
    We are the scoffer's creed;
We are the Lord's last message,
    Given in deed and word;
What if the type is crooked?
    What if the print is blurred?

What if our hands are busy
    With other work than His?
What if our feet are walking
    Where sin's allurement is?
What if our tongues are speaking
    Of things His lips would spurn?
How can we hope to help him
    And hasten his return?

---

scoffer—*someone who mocks*
creed—*a statement of what one believes*
allurement—*attraction*

The Silver Coin

Laurel Hicks

J. Hudson Taylor, the famous missionary to China of the 1800s, was known as a man who depended completely on God for all his needs. He is called the Father of Faith Missions. He did not tell people about his needs for money and supplies for his missionary work. Instead, he told God about it in prayer and asked God to move people to give as much as was needed. "To move men through God by prayer" was his motto.

Hudson learned to depend on God for everything when he was a young man of nineteen. He knew that God had called him to China, and he began to prepare himself by working for a Christian doctor in Hull, England, about 50 miles from his hometown. He wanted to learn all he could about medicine so he could better minister to the Chinese people.

"This is a serious matter," he wrote to his sister Amelia. "If I am to go to China, I must be ready. Not only do I need to prepare my mind, but I must also learn to endure hardness and to trust God alone for everything."

To practice enduring hardness, Hudson left the comfortable home where lodging and meals had been provided for him and moved into a small, inexpensive room in a part of town where the poorer people lived. It was lonely here, but much easier to find time for Bible reading and prayer. He was closer to the homes of the poor people whom he visited and witnessed to every Sunday, too, and by living with these people he could better know how to meet their spiritual needs. With the money he saved by living here and fixing his own simple meals, he could help them with their physical needs, also.

Hudson had a real test of his faith one time when the doctor for whom he worked forgot to pay him. "I will not remind him," he thought to himself. "Instead, I'll ask God to remind him. I know that my Heavenly Father will take care of me."

Days went by, and still Hudson had no paycheck. After paying his landlady for his rent on Saturday night, he found that all he had left was one silver coin, called a half crown. It was worth perhaps a dollar in our money. He checked his cupboard and found he had enough food to last through Monday morning. "The half crown will buy my lunch and dinner on Monday," he thought to himself, "so I have no need to worry. I'll just keep asking God for the money I will need for the rest of the week."

The next day was Sunday, so Hudson got up, ate breakfast, and went to church as usual. During the afternoon and evening, he visited the homes and boarding houses of the poor people around him, telling the people of God's love for

boarding houses—*houses where rooms can be rented*

them and His provision for their eternal salvation. He kept this up until ten o'clock at night and then gathered his Bible and gospel tracts together in preparation for returning home. Glancing up, he saw a sad, weary-looking man shuffle toward him.

"Please, sir," pleaded the stranger, "would you come to my home and pray with my wife? She is seriously ill, and I fear she will not live until morning."

"I will come and do what I can," Hudson replied. As he followed the ragged stranger out to the street and down dark, narrow lanes, Hudson felt the silver coin in his pocket. He remembered that there was nothing in his cupboard but a bowl of watered-down oatmeal—enough for supper tonight and breakfast in the morning. If his half crown were stolen, he would have no money for tomorrow's lunch and dinner.

But still he followed on, and suddenly the stranger turned into a dark courtyard that Hudson recognized. How could he forget his last visit here? The occupants of the shabby rooms had torn up his tracts and told him never to come back with his Jesus preaching. "If we see you here again, you will be sorry!" they shouted.

"And here I am again," thought Hudson, "with a man whose story may or may not be true." He sighed, and then groped his way up a narrow, rickety flight of stairs behind the stranger. A door creaked open, and what a sight met his eyes!

Four or five ragged, barefoot children with sunken cheeks and grimy, torn clothes were standing in the drafty room or lying on the floor. "The poor things!" Hudson thought. "They'll starve to death if no one helps them!" Again he fingered the silver coin in his pocket. "If only it were in smaller change," he told himself, "surely I would give *half* of it to this needy family!"

Then he saw the woman lying on a straw mattress on the floor. A tiny baby less than two days old lay moaning by her side. It was clear that neither of them could live without food.

Hudson began to tell the family about God's love and salvation. "Don't worry," he said; "just trust in God for all your needs."

In his heart, Hudson heard God chiding him: "Hudson Taylor, why are you telling these poor people to trust in me when you don't even believe I can take care of you without the help of that silver coin in your pocket?"

"If only I had change for my half crown," Hudson replied, "I would give *three fourths* of it to these people." He then knelt down and prayed aloud for the family, but he had a difficult time finding words for his prayer. The joy had left his heart, and he had an empty, troubled feeling within.

Rising from his knees, he turned to face the father. "Please, sir," the man pleaded, "you see what a desperate state we are in. If you can help us, please do—for the sake of your Lord!"

Just then the words of Jesus flashed into Hudson's mind: "Give to him that asketh thee . . ." (Matt. 5:42). Knowing that he must obey his King, Hudson reached slowly into his pocket, pulled out the silver coin, and handed it to the man.

"It is not much," said Hudson, "but believe me, it is all that I have. What I have been trying to tell you is true. God *is* a loving Father, and He *can* be trusted."

Immediately the burden on his heart was gone, and joy flooded his soul. As he walked home along the lonely, deserted streets, a hymn of praise sprang from his lips.

His supper of watery oatmeal before bed seemed to him a feast fit for a prince. "Dear Lord," he prayed, kneeling by his bed, "Your Word says that the one who gives to the poor is lending to you. Please, Father, would you let the loan be a short one so I can have dinner tomorrow?"

The next morning, after a peaceful sleep, Hudson sat down to eat the last of his oatmeal. Before he finished, he heard the postman's knock on the outside door. Soon his landlady came into the room and handed him a small packet.

"I wonder who could have sent this?" he asked himself. "The handwriting is not familiar, and the postmark is blurred." There was no note or letter inside, just a pair of new gloves. As he pulled them out to examine them, something fell with a ringing sound to the floor.

"What was that?" he said aloud as he reached down to retrieve the shiny object. "A gold coin! Why, this is worth *four times* as much as the silver coin I gave away! Thank you, Lord. You *do* keep Your word! I can trust You, not only with my money, but with all of my life! If I can rely on You here in England, then I can rely on You in China, too!"

Two years later, in 1853, Hudson Taylor boarded a ship for China. He quickly learned the difficult Chinese language and mastered such Chinese customs as eating with chopsticks. Nothing must hinder his being used of God among these people. He began to dress in the Chinese manner, and he even shaved off most of his hair, leaving only a single pigtail, in the style of all Chinese men of that day. Most important, he told no one of his needs—no one but God, that is—and God moved His people to give.

In 1865, Hudson Taylor founded the China Inland Mission, which was based on the principle of telling God, not people, of needs for money and supplies. By the time of his death in 1905, there were 849 "faith missionaries" in China and 125,000 Chinese Christians.

The example of this great man of faith continues to encourage missionaries and other Christian workers throughout the world to walk closely with God and depend on Him to supply their needs. Hudson Taylor's life encourages Christian people everywhere to give cheerfully to God's work, knowing that God will take care of them.

> *"For your Father knoweth*
> *what things ye have need of,*
> *before ye ask Him."*
> —Matthew 6:8

Time to Think

1. How did Hudson Taylor practice enduring hardness?
2. How did Mr. Taylor end up with only one silver coin?
3. What made him wish the coin were in smaller change?
4. How did God show faithfulness when Mr. Taylor gave the whole coin away?
5. What are some things you can trust God for today?

If You Were

Author Unknown

If you were busy being kind,
Before you knew it, you would find
You'd soon forget to think 'twas true
That someone was unkind to you.

If you were busy being glad,
And cheering people who are sad,
Although your heart might ache a bit,
You'd soon forget to notice it.

If you were busy being good,
And doing just the best you could,
You'd not have time to blame some man
Who's doing just the best he can.

If you were busy being right,
You'd find yourself too busy quite
To criticize your neighbor long
Because he's busy being wrong.

When the
Morning Star Sailed

Grace W. McGavran

America is great because of the blessing of
God. One reason God has blessed America is
the large number of missionaries who have left
our shores to take the gospel to other lands.

The *Morning Star* set her sails to the wind and slipped
out of old Boston Harbor. She was a special kind of vessel—
a missionary ship. The children of the Congregational
churches had her for their very own ship, to carry missionaries to far off islands and to visit them and carry supplies to
them from time to time.

On the rough dock there were a group of people whose lips moved silently in prayer as the good ship sailed farther and farther from them. They prayed for those on board for a safe voyage first, and for their welfare in the cannibal islands of the South Seas after their journey was over.

On board, the passengers felt a strange thrill. They were leaving home and country and friends, perhaps never to see them again. Like Paul, they were going to strange places and among unfriendly people. Like him, they had just one purpose in mind and that was to carry the gospel to the islands of the South Seas.

Young Hiram Bingham, just twenty-five years old, and his wife, who was younger, stood together by the ship's rail. They had all the courage of their ancestors who had come to America, then an unknown land. Now they themselves were going to an unknown country and they hoped to make it a Christian land before they died.

On sailed the ship. Far to the south it went, till it came to the tip of South America. Around the tip it went, and then turned north and west. On and on and on! Finally it came to a group of islands that we now call Hawaii.

There Hiram Bingham and his wife landed. They were going to stay there for a few months before going on.

Hiram was no stranger to the Hawaiian Islands. He had been born there and he loved the place. His father had gone there as a missionary. Hiram had watched his father translate the Bible into the Hawaiian language. He had even done his small share to help by carrying pages to the printer.

---

welfare—*the condition*

At last the time came to go on from Hawaii. The *Morning Star,* which spent its time sailing from one missionary outpost to another, was ready to set out for the Gilbert Islands. Those islands were a thousand miles to the southwest of Hawaii. They lay like tiny jewels in the vast Pacific. It was to one of them that Hiram and his wife were to go. Across the thousand miles of ocean the ship sailed steadily with her passengers.

Once more the gallant little *Morning Star* came to anchor. But this time it was within the reef of a lagoon on the island of Apaiang. Hiram Bingham and his wife were ready to disembark. Their few possessions were lowered and taken to the beach in the ship's rowboat.

The shores were lined with dark-skinned natives. Their faces were not unfriendly, for another missionary couple had visited them during the previous year. The king was willing to have Hiram come because he realized that the missionary people were different from the crews of the trading boats who so often in those days carried off strong young boys to sell into slavery. His people were ready to murder the crews of such boats without any hesitation, but the missionaries had made a different impression.

Along with their chests, the *Morning Star* unloaded materials for building a simple house in which Hiram and his wife could live.

---

gallant—*brave and noble*
reef—*a ridge of rock or coral in a body of water*
Apaiang (ə·pŏ′ē·ăng)
disembark—*to get off a ship*

Then the sails were hoisted. The little ship slipped quietly out from behind the reef, and the two young people were left on an island a thousand miles from Hawaii. They were surrounded by other little islands on which lived hostile people. They did not know whether, when the *Morning Star* came again next year, they would be there to welcome it or not.

Now came the business of learning the language spoken by the people of the Gilbert Islands. There was just one way to do it. Hiram would point to an object. An islander would give the name for it in his language. Hiram would repeat the word the islander said. Then he would point to something else and get its name. That word would be repeated. He would hear a mother shout to her child, and the child would reply and come running. He wondered whether the mother had said, "Dinner!" or "Bad boy, come here!" or "Quick, I need help!"

That was something to guess at. But by listening and watching and questioning, Hiram and his wife learned more and more words. They learned phrases and even sentences.

But how were the words to be put into writing? Hiram and his wife had to make an alphabet. Then they could put into writing the new words and phrases they had learned.

They began to try to find out words for the ideas in the Gospel of Matthew and to translate that book of the Bible. It helped a lot for Hiram to know how his father had gone about the job in Hawaii. He knew what mistakes not to make, and some of the shortcuts. But just the same it took a long time.

---

hoisted—*raised or put up*

At last twelve chapters of the Gospel were done. A visiting sailing ship carried the manuscript back across a thousand miles of ocean to Hawaii. There the chapters were printed. It took months, but oh, what a thrill it was to Hiram and his wife when another vessel came out of its way to bring those printed pages to Apaiang!

Meanwhile Hiram and his wife had been teaching the people as well as learning the language. They had helpers now from among the people of the island. Hiram had even visited some of the nearby unfriendly islands and talked to their people about the message of Jesus. While the first chapters were being printed, he had gone on translating the rest of the Gospel of Matthew.

It was not too long before the whole Gospel of Matthew had been sent to Hawaii for printing. More months went by. Then one day, white sails appeared on the horizon, and a ship laid its course straight for Apaiang! Every person was down on the beach to meet it, for the Christians of the little island were as eager to see the printed Gospel as were the Binghams. They supposed, of course, that the ship was bringing it.

But no! The ship brought a message instead, and a disappointing one. The printers of Hawaii were too busy to publish the book. Instead, they had what they thought was a brilliant idea. They sent the manuscript back. Along with it they sent a little printing press in a box with type and ink and paper. "Print the Gospel yourselves!" they wrote. "And you can print other things, too, and not have to wait so long for them."

Hiram stared at the box. He didn't know one single thing about printing presses. He felt very gloomy.

After the visiting ship was gone, Hiram and his wife unpacked the press. But they could not figure out how it worked, and there was nothing they could do about it. They would have to wait until another ship came and send the manuscript of Matthew once more to Hawaii to be printed. They felt so disappointed that they could hardly speak to each other about the press.

One morning two days later, a small boy shouted loudly to Hiram, "Quick! Quick! A boat is coming!"

Hiram and his wife rushed out of their house. They could hardly believe their eyes. There across the little lagoon that was sheltered from the rolling waves of the ocean, a tiny rowboat was being pulled toward them.

They rushed down to the beach.

The weary rowers looked as astonished as Hiram.

"Where's your ship?" shouted Hiram.

"Wrecked and gone down in the storm," answered the men, who, he could see now, were sailors. "We four are all who are saved. We landed on another island and heard that here we could get a ship that would take us home."

The shipwrecked men were as thankful as they were astonished to find a missionary and his wife and a Christian group of people on the island. They ate eagerly the food that was prepared for them. They needed sleep and rest almost as much as food.

As soon as they had recovered from their perilous experience, the four men wandered around the island, giving a hand with whatever Hiram set them to doing. One of them, whose name was Hotchkiss, came upon the printing press.

"What's this!" he exclaimed. "Do you print things here on this island?"

"No," and Hiram sadly explained what had happened.

Hotchkiss smiled broadly. "I'm a printer," said he, "and in no time at all I'll have this little beauty of a hand press working. Give me what it is you want printed. I'll do it, and show you how, too," he added.

Hiram was overjoyed. "It is God himself who sent you," said he.

Busy days followed. Hotchkiss set up the press. When a sailing vessel came by and took away the other shipwrecked men, he stayed to finish the printing and to teach Hiram and his islanders the art of managing the press.

So there came into the hands of the islanders of Apaiang the whole book of Matthew in their own language. And after that the Gospel of John, and the Epistle to the Ephesians. More could not be printed then, for there was only a small amount of paper. But Hiram and his wife rejoiced every time they saw one of those precious copies in the hands of an earnestly reading islander.

The Bible had come to the Gilbert Islands.

The years went by, and all the people in the Gilbert Islands became Christians. The year 1892 is one to remember, for in that year Hiram Bingham finished the translation of the whole Bible.

He did not try to print it on the island. The manuscript was sent to New York, to the American Bible Society, and they printed it. Hiram and his wife went to New York for the reading of the proofs.

The Bible was printed in 1893.

The precious plates, from which the printing is done when new copies are needed, lie in the fireproof vault of the American Bible Society's building in New York. They are the only plates of the Bible in Gilbertese in all the world, and no one wants to risk their getting destroyed.

So, today when Gilbertese Bibles are needed, a message goes from the islands to New York. The Bibles are packed and taken to a ship. Soon they are on their way across the rolling ocean waves to the islands where long years ago the *Morning Star* dropped anchor. And on those islands, where Hiram Bingham and his wife lived and worked so bravely, a Christian people today reads in its own language the message of God's love.

Time to Think

1. Why weren't the people of Apaiang afraid of the missionaries?
2. How did the Binghams learn to speak the islander's language?
3. Why were Hiram and his wife so disappointed when the manuscript was sent back with a printing press?
4. Who did God use to show Hiram how to use the press?
5. What did Hiram and his wife finally accomplish in 1893?

Sunder
of India

Janet Woehrer (adapted)

"Home is better than this," Sunder grumbled, as she stood in front of the schoolroom at a mission in India.

She looked over at the wall that surrounded the school and some of the other buildings of the mission. Sunder knew that the wall was for the protection of those inside and that the gate was locked only at night. But to her it seemed like a prison wall that kept her in a place she didn't want to be.

Sunder's name means *pretty* in her language, but right now the deep frown on her face made her look anything but pretty. For the moment she had forgotten that home hadn't always been a happy place, either.

Sunder always wanted to have her own way, and her parents often had to scold her or punish her for the things she did. But no matter how much her parents had corrected her, Sunder just wouldn't be any better. She became such a problem that her parents had finally sent her to the school run by the missionaries.

These missionaries had come from a land far across the sea to tell the people of India about the true and living God and His Son, whom they called the Lord Jesus Christ. The

Sunder (sōōn′dər)

225

people who believed in this Lord Jesus Christ were called Christians. There were some of these believers, or Christians, in Sunder's village.

When she thought of the Christians in her village, the frown on Sunder's face got even deeper. The people in her village didn't like it when one of their people believed in this God, and they were not kind to them. They would not let the Christians draw water from the village well, and this was the only place in the whole village where they could get water.

"I don't want to hear about this God the Christians worship," she said to herself.

Quietly she slipped into the classroom and sat down at her desk. But she wasn't thinking about her studies. "Who cares about numbers, anyhow! I can count on the knuckles of my fingers and on my toes. Is this not enough?"

"I know what I will do," she thought. "If these people will not let me go, I will make up a lie. Even though my mother sent me here and my father insists that I stay, I will not stay. These people's ways are not my ways, and I don't like it here!"

Suddenly Sunder jumped up and shouted at the teacher. "Why did you make me drink chalk water? You knew it was poisonous!"

She saw the surprised look on the face of her teacher.

"What on earth are you talking about?" the teacher asked in a puzzled voice.

"Why did you make me drink chalk water? You knew it was poisonous!" Sunder said again.

And to herself she smirked, "There, I guess I gave her something to think about. She knows if this story gets back

to my village the
people will be only too
glad to believe it. Then they will
do something to harm the Christians in the village, too."

Instead of scolding Sunder, the teacher took her into the principal's office.

"This is good," Sunder thought, as she looked defiantly at the principal. "She'll be afraid, too. Now I'm sure they will let me go if I promise not to tell this awful story."

But the principal didn't even look disturbed about it as Sunder again accused the teacher of giving her poisoned chalk water. "Sunder," she said, "if your teacher caused you to drink chalk water that was poisoned, you would not be alive now."

Sunder felt foolish, but she held her head up high as she went back to her class. Surely there must be some way to get out of this place. Oh, yes! Why hadn't she thought of that before? Why, she'd simply run away. She was sure she was clever enough to get away without anybody catching her.

The next morning during prayer time at the school, Sunder saw her chance. While the others had their heads bowed and eyes closed, she tiptoed outside and walked toward the gate. No one was around. This seemed so easy, but she knew she had to be careful, for there were other buildings outside the wall.

As she went out the gate, she was thinking, "I have no money, but I will beg. I will tell such good lies that people will feel sorry for me. Then they will give me money to help with my bus fare. I'll make them think I have lost my money and cannot get home to my parents."

As Sunder came near the big house outside the wall, she saw the missionary whom everyone lovingly called "Aunty" inside getting her hair cut.

Sunder began to walk faster. "I hope she will not look up and see me!"

As she passed the house, Sunder noticed the big bell on the veranda. It was used to call the servants when they were needed in a hurry. She began to run down the driveway toward the back road.

Suddenly the bell began to ring.

"Oh," Sunder groaned. "Aunty did see me! Now they'll be after me right away." She gave a quick look over her shoulder, and coming out of the mission yard was the gardener.

"Oh, my," Sunder groaned. "He can run faster than I can."

Hardly able to breathe, she ran as fast as she could.

Closer and closer came the heavy, pounding feet.

Sunder felt the gardener's hard, strong hand clamp down on her shoulder.

"Let me go! Let me go!" she screamed. She kept kicking and screaming as the gardener pulled her back to the house where the missionary was.

Sunder thought the missionary was going to whip her. And that would have been all right, for then maybe her parents would let her come home if she said the missionary beat her.

But the missionary didn't whip her. Instead, she talked to her kindly about the Lord Jesus. She reminded Sunder that it was for her, Sunder's, sin that He had died on the cross. But Sunder wasn't paying any attention to that. She decided to tell a lie that would touch the missionary's soft heart.

"I had an awful dream," she said pitifully. "I just knew from it that my parents were very ill and I had to go quickly to see them."

The missionary shook her head sadly. "I just had a letter from your father asking that we keep you here at the school so you can learn to obey and learn some of the things they could not teach you at home."

Sunder was disgusted. There just wasn't anything more she could do—or was there? Her eyes narrowed as she began thinking of a plan that would surely work!

She had heard of somebody who had pretended to be crazy and got a free ticket to the next town, for no one wanted a crazy person around. She made a face that she thought was her best crazy look. She began to cry and twist her face into the worst expressions she could think of.

"Sunder," the missionary spoke firmly. "We have had enough of this nonsense. As long as your parents want you to stay here, we will keep you here and try to help you."

A few days later a letter came from her parents. Sunder could hardly believe what she read.

Why, her father said they had been listening to the people who talked about the living God and that they were seriously thinking about this Christian religion.

Did this mean her parents were believers in this new God? Would they be stopped from getting water from the village well? And would the grocer tell them they could not buy food from his store, as he had done to the other Christians? This would mean they would have to go to the next village some distance away for their food and water!

Surely her parents wouldn't believe in this strange God!

Sunder didn't know what to do. She wondered what was happening to her parents, but for a while she didn't try any more schemes to get sent home.

Then one evening at five o'clock, when she heard the small bell that rang to call the Christians to prayer, she remembered that one day she had noticed a crack in the wall that was around the school. She had heard that once a man had climbed over the wall that way because he wanted to steal some food from the storehouse.

"So, the crack would be big enough for my toes," Sunder thought, as she wiggled them in the soft dirt. But she knew that if she were going to try that, she would have to do it quickly, for she had heard the missionaries talking about getting the crack fixed.

"I'm sure they would never think any of us girls would try that," she smirked.

Sunder lingered behind until the others had all gone to the prayer meeting. The she sauntered over toward the wall, looking carefully around to see that no one was in sight.

But she forgot that the servants would be outside the kitchen at the large hearth where the food was being kept warm for the evening meal. Carefully she put one foot in the crack of the wall. She gave herself a big push and barely grasped the top of the wall with her hands, but just as she was pulling herself up to the top of the wall, she felt a firm grip around her waist. Sunder clung to the wall with all her might, but the servant firmly pulled her down.

Feeling disgusted, she made her way to her room, but it was lonely there. She might just as well go over to the meeting and see what was going on. At least it might be entertaining.

The group was singing a hymn when Sunder came in. Quietly she sat down on a mat in back. She thought the singing was beautiful, and she admitted to herself, "I have never heard such quiet and worshipful music in my village. It is doing something to my heart."

When the others bowed their heads to pray, Sunder just sat there thinking. And what she thought of most was that *Jesus really lives.*

Suddenly, Sunder heard her name, and she began to listen to the girls as they prayed. She was surprised that they were talking about her; then she realized that they had not heard her come in.

The girls asked God to show her that she needed a clean heart. *A clean heart?* Sunder knew that when these Christians spoke of a clean heart, or a new heart, they didn't mean the heart that is a part of our bodies. They really meant our life; the part of us that thinks, and loves, or gets angry. We can't see this part of us, but it is what makes us do the things we do. This is the part of us that sins—does wrong things too.

Sunder knew she had done many, many things that were not right—she had disobeyed her parents, she had gotten angry, she had told lies, she had done many bad things just to get her own way. Now she could hardly stand it as she heard the Christian girls talking to their God about her. What if this God really heard?

232

"We pray to our many wooden gods," Sunder thought, "but they do not hear. I know, for they do not answer. But if this Lord Jesus Christ can make people different, I would like that. I am tired of being so mean that no one really likes me."

Softly Sunder began to weep. Even though she had been mean, these girls cared enough to pray for her and to ask God to help her. Sunder couldn't see God, as she could see the wooden idols, but somehow she knew then that He was hearing the prayers of these girls. And in her heart she wondered, "Would He listen to a rascal like me?"

After prayers, Sunder looked around and saw two girls near her reading from the book they called the Word of God. Finally one of them looked up, and a look of surprise came on her face when she saw Sunder. She spoke to the other girl, and they both motioned to Sunder to come and read with them.

Sunder moved over with the girls. One of them pointed to John 3:16 and whispered, "Put your name where the word *whosoever* is."

Sunder read the verse to herself ". . . God so loved the world, that He gave His only begotten Son, that whosoever believeth—no, not whosoever, but Sunder—if Sunder believes in Him she should not perish, but have everlasting life."

Sunder wondered with joy if this was really true. "Did God love me enough to give His only Son, the Lord Jesus, to die for me?"

Later that evening Sunder went to the office of the missionary whom they all called "Aunty." Shyly she stood in the door, finding it hard to look up.

"Come in and sit near me," Aunty said kindly.

Aunty sat in a chair,
and Sunder sat on a mat on the
floor as the people in her village did.

Looking up into Aunty's kind face, Sundered whispered, "I
want to ask you to forgive me for giving you nothing but
trouble. And please pray for me that I will be a good girl," she
added hastily.

Right out loud Aunty said, "Praise the Lord." Then Aunty
prayed for Sunder, asking God to help her understand what
the Lord Jesus Christ had done for her and to help her receive
Him as her Savior.

Aunty gave Sunder a New Testament and showed her some of the places that would be best for her to read first. Gladly Sunder took the New Testament and went right to her room. Sitting on the floor, she began to read from God's Word, forgetting all about eating. As the light of the setting sun began to fade, Sunder lit a small lamp and read far into the night.

First, she read that "all have sinned" (Romans 3:23). *All* meant everybody. And Sunder knew it meant her, too. Then Sunder read "The wages of sin is death" (Romans 6:23). That meant that the payment, or result, of sin was death. And Sunder had heard the Christians say that this death was different from the death of the body. It meant that after the body died, the real person that lives inside the body could not go to heaven to live with God. "Oh," thought Sunder, "that would be awful."

But right away Sunder read again the verse that told her that the Lord Jesus Christ had died for her—that He had already taken the payment, or punishment, for her sins.

And right there and then, Sunder believed that the Lord Jesus, the Son of the true and living God, had died for *her* sins, that He arose from the dead and was living again in Heaven. And she believed in Him; she received Him as her very own Saviour.

The next day Sunder went right to her teacher and asked her to forgive her for trying to get her into trouble. The teacher put her arm around Sunder and hugged her. Sunder knew that the teacher forgave her, and her own heart was full of love for the teacher, instead of hate as it had been before.

Whenever Sunder was tempted to do the wrong things she had done for so long, she would remember to ask the Lord Jesus to help her. As she read and obeyed God's Word, she lost her temper less often, and she found that many of the things she wanted to have her own way in weren't really important. She also found that it was much nicer to be kind and helpful and to share with others. The other girls began to like to have Sunder with them, and they had many good times together.

One day, the missionary told her that her father was coming to the mission to visit.

"What will happen?" Sunder wondered. Was Father coming to take her home? Should she tell him she was now a Christian, and that she wanted to stay here?

When Sunder's father arrived, almost the first thing he said was, "Your face looks more like your name now, Daughter." And although Sunder didn't realize it, when she began to change inside, her face no longer looked mean and pouty, and did indeed look pretty.

"Oh, Father," Sunder exclaimed, "if my face is pretty, it is only because the Lord Jesus made it that way." Without thinking, she told him about receiving the Lord Jesus as her Saviour, and she showed him John 3:16 in her New Testament.

Then her heart began to beat faster. What would Father think? Would he be angry with her?

But Father didn't become angry. Instead, he told her that he, too, had received the Lord Jesus as his Savior, but he had been afraid to tell anyone. How glad Sunder was to know Father was a Christian, too!

Father stayed at the mission a few days, and he learned that the Lord Jesus could keep peace in his heart. Then he was no longer afraid, but wanted to let people know he was now a Christian.

After her father returned home, Sunder began to count the days until she could go home, too. Finally vacation time came, and Sunder climbed into the two-wheeled cart, pulled by two white bulls, that was to take her and the other children to the train.

As they jogged along, Sunder wondered if she had put everything that she needed into her little tin suitcase. She had carefully folded the long skirt they had given her at the mission, and today she was wearing her old sari, a very long piece of cloth which the Indian women and girls wrap loosely around the body, draping one end gracefully over one shoulder or up over the head.

Along with the skirt, she had put into the little tin suitcase her report card, what was left of a bar of soap, and her bottle of hair oil. The hot India sun made their black hair so dry and dull that the girls had to use the hair oil to keep it bright and pretty. And the comb—some of the teeth were missing, but it was still a good comb, and much used now to keep her long hair neat. Sunder smiled as she thought how surprised her friends would be to see how neat and clean she kept herself, when before she really hadn't cared whether she was neat or not. But most of all she hoped they would see that she had changed in her actions, too.

What else? Oh, yes, her New Testament and her songbook. Aunty had marked in the New Testament for her the verses that had helped her come to Jesus.

Before long they were on the train. It was a long journey, but finally they were at her station, and there was her father to meet her.

While she was home on vacation, Sunder tried to tell her friends about the Lord Jesus.

At first two of her friends, Venu and Punchphoola (pronounced Vay noo and Punch poola), made fun of her because she was different. They knew she had always told the biggest lies of any of them, but now she wouldn't lie any more. One day they wanted her to go with them to steal some squash from a neighbor's garden. When Sunder refused, they thought she was crazy. Why, it was great fun to try to steal without getting caught.

"But it is wrong," Sunder told them.

"Wrong?" both girls asked. And one added, "Nothing is wrong until you are caught at it, is it?"

Sunder asked them if they thought God knew better than people did. They were not sure. Then Sunder reminded them that she knew the God who *lived*—One who sees what we do, and who cares about us, and who answers prayer.

Sunder saw that the girls were getting interested. She showed them in her New Testament that God says "all have sinned" (Romans 3:23). Both girls agreed to that. But when she told them they had to have their sins forgiven before they could go to heaven, Venu sneered and said, "If there is a long piece of hair down the back of the head and your hand is on a cow's tail when you die, you will go to heaven."

In India people worship the cow, and no one is allowed to kill one. There are many, many cows in the streets of the villages and towns. Sunder had believed all these things about the cows once, too, but now she knew the true way to get to heaven.

Sunder also showed the girls the other verses that were marked in her New Testament and explained each one. Venu thought it was wonderful, and she said she wanted to receive the Lord Jesus.

Punchphoola shrugged. "It is a nice story, but right now I want to go steal some squash."

Sadly Sunder watched Punchphoola walk away.

Then she and Venu bowed their heads. Venu wasn't quite sure what to say, but she did tell God she was sorry for her sins, and that she believed the Lord Jesus had died for her sins. And she did receive Him as her Saviour.

How happy Sunder was to show her friend how to receive the Lord Jesus! And how glad both were that they knew the true and living God who hears and answers prayer.

Time to Think

1. Why was Sunder sent to the missionary school?
2. Why did Sunder accuse the teacher of making her drink chalk water?
3. Why didn't Sunder want her parents to believe in God?
4. When did Sunder finally realize that God could change her life?
5. Name some things that changed in Sunder's life after she was saved.

The Decisions of Byang Kato
Sophie de la Haye (adapted)

"Scat, you birds, scat!" The high-pitched voice of young Byang Kato echoed through the hills under the hot African sun. Suddenly, all was quiet, for the bird scarer had dropped wearily into the shade of the kuka tree. He knew it was his responsibility to keep the birds from plucking away his father's crops, but Father was nowhere in sight, and Byang chose to rest awhile.

Byang Kato (bē′yäng kā′tō′)   **kuka** (kōō′kə)

Although Byang was old enough to attend school, there was no school in his village in northern Nigeria. When he was not helping his parents, he spent his time with friends making model cars and planes from dried cornstalks and clay, fishing and swimming in the river, or climbing rocky hills to play war with slingshots and bows and arrows.

When he was ten years old, the excited Byang joined 300 other boys for an initiation with the older men of the Jaba tribe. The boys were escorted into the jungle for secret rites that would make them men. They spent days in a huge cave and nights in a sacred grove where trees, bushes, and vines were never cut. After seven days of very secret activities, the boys returned to the village, where they were welcomed with singing and drumming. People had gathered from miles around bringing goats, sheep, and chickens to offer as sacrifices to the spirits.

As the weeks passed, Byang grew more and more disappointed. He had thought that becoming a real man would bring happiness to him, but somehow there was still an empty place in his heart that he longed to have filled.

Then one day a strange-looking woman came into the village struggling under the weight of a black box. "The box laughs and talks and sings!" said some of the smaller children. "There's a man inside!" Byang told them. The missionary returned to the village many times, each time bringing the old black record player with her. Byang carried it on his head back to the missionary's home while she told him more

---

Nigeria (nī·jĭr′ē·ə)

‘tiation—*the act or ceremony that permits membership in a group*

‥·bə′)

‘emonies

about the true God Who sent His Son to be our Savior. Soon Byang was going to Sunday school and to a boys' club held in a nearby church.

When Byang was eleven, he persuaded his father to let him go to the mission school, promising to get up extra early every morning and help on the farm first. This arrangement lasted only a few months, however. The workload on the farm increased, and his father forced Byang to leave school to help him full-time.

The next year, an African pastor, knowing of Byang's great hunger to learn, pleaded with the boy's parents to let him return to the school. "He may go, but we will not pay," they finally said. Byang, determined to earn his own way, worked for the missionaries—gardening, cleaning, sweeping the front yard, carrying water from the well, and doing other odd jobs.

One day, Byang's Nigerian teacher told the class about Noah and the ark. Even though Byang was twelve years old, he had never heard this story before, and he was fascinated. The teacher told how Noah and his family made the decision to enter the ark because they believed God, while the other people chose to refuse God's place of refuge. "Choose you this day whom you will serve," God's Word says.

When the teacher told about God closing the door and then described the rain and the floodwaters, Byang thought about the people outside the ark. They died in the flood because they chose not to heed God's warning! The teacher explained about God's punishment for sin: "The wages of sin is death." Byang listened closely as he heard once again that God's perfect Son, Jesus Christ, had shed His own blood to take the eternal punishment for our sin.

Suddenly, Byang knew he must make a decision. "I realize that I am a sinner," he said, as he stood before the class. "I choose to receive God's free gift of salvation in Jesus Christ."

Byang's mother noticed a difference in her son when he returned home. "He is so obedient," she told the neighbors. "He goes to the river for water, borrows live coals to start a fire, and helps around the house without complaining."

The neighbors, too, soon noticed the difference in Byang. "He is unselfish," they said. "If he has something to eat, he gladly shares it." This was not like most Jaba boys, who thought only of getting things for themselves. Byang eagerly took part in the boys' club activities—choir, Scripture memory, and drilling in acrobatics and marching. He went regularly to Sunday school and church, often persuading other boys to go with him.

One person was not pleased with the change in Byang. "I give you food and clothing," Byang's father told him.

"You must give up this new religion." Byang's father beat him, thinking that would make him change his mind, but Byang had made the decision to leave his old ways and follow Jesus Christ. He would not turn back. As a testimony of his new life in Christ, he went to a nearby stream and was baptized with 300 other Christians.

A few months later, Byang listened as Pastor Gin told of villages where people had not yet heard the gospel. "You are doing nothing to share this message with your brothers and sisters. You are selfish," Pastor Gin scolded the Christians. The spirit of God spoke to hearts. One after another, people in the audience got up from the mud-plastered benches where they were seated. Some gave pieces of clothing. Others emptied all the money from their pockets as they went forward to show they would keep nothing back from the Lord. Others promised to give personal belongings like pigs and goats. Day after day the meetings continued.

Byang responded too. "My heart is breaking within me," he said. "I have been selfish. I have not shared the good news of Jesus Christ with enough people."

Later, as Pastor Gin spoke about the love of things, Byang felt convicted again. "I am wearing an undershirt and a shirt, and I have another shirt at home." He placed his shirt on the altar as a symbol of his dedication.

As he did so, it seemed the Lord said to him, "It's not only your shirt I want. I want your life."

"Lord, I give You my life. I don't know what You want me to be, but I dedicate myself to You," Byang prayed. After this, Byang worked harder than ever on his studies, and he soon ranked first in his class. He became a leader in the boys' club at church, using his spare time to train younger boys in Christian living.

Then the time came for Byang to choose a college. Should he go to the regular college that many of his classmates had chosen to attend, or should he go to a Bible college and train for Christian service? Despite pressure from his classmates to follow their lead, Byang chose to attend a Bible college 300 miles from home.

"You will be poor all your life," some of his friends jeered. "Being a pastor is for old men, not for a young man who has the brains to make it elsewhere."

One day while working in a missionary's home, Byang read a wall plaque:

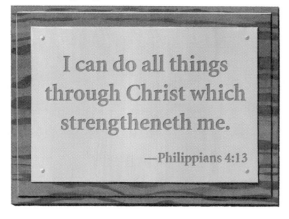

I can do all things through Christ which strengtheneth me.

—Philippians 4:13

"That's it!" Byang said. "I will make this verse my life motto. I know I have made the right choice in preparing to serve God."

As the time drew near to leave for Bible school, Byang was trusting God to supply the money he needed for school and for train fare. "I don't know how God will do it, but I cannot ask relatives or friends. I will only ask God." The last week before it was time to leave for college, an envelope came through the mail. There was enough money in it for his ticket! "Thank you, Lord. Now, I'm trusting You for the money for college. I'm sure it is Your plan that I go."

A few days later his pastor announced, "Byang, the people of the church have decided to pay your fees for the first year." Byang's heart was full of joy and praise as he began his journey.

Byang's parents had been trying to arrange for him to marry a girl who was not a Christian, but Byang knew that this was not God's will. He prayed that God would lead him to the right wife for him. During his second year at Bible school, Byang wrote to Jummai, a Christian girl from his home church. "I have prayed a long time about God's choice," he said in the letter, "and now I know that you are the one God wants me to ask to marry me."

Jummai was in agreement, and the two were married in their home church. As Jummai walked down the aisle with a beautiful smile, Byang turned completely around and watched her come toward him. His eyes lighted up; his face beamed. He knew he had made another right choice—a Christian wife.

The next day, Byang and his young wife left for Bible school, and Byang worked harder than ever before. From the beginning of their married life, the couple read the Bible and prayed together every day. "Byang and Jummai show what a Christian home should be like," a neighbor said; "they never seem to frown or talk harshly to each other."

After graduation, Byang taught in Bible school for a while, but he soon realized that he needed more education.

Jummai (jo͞o·mā′)

He took courses by correspondence, and two years later he received a scholarship to attend a college in England. Byang and Jummai had three children now—Deborah, Jonathan, and little Paul.

After his studies in England, Byang went to Paris, France, for a three-month course on teaching the Bible to children. As he sat in the classes, he learned that even small children were sinners and needed to receive Christ as their Savior. He thought of all the children in his own country who had never had a chance to hear of Jesus. "Who will tell them?" he asked Jummai. Then the couple thought of their own children. "Dear Lord," they prayed, "please help us to lead Deborah, Jonathan, and Paul to trust in You."

In January, during family devotions, Jonathan received Christ as his Savior from sin. In February, Deborah became a Christian. They continued to pray for Paul, who was six years old. It was Easter time, and the Katos were discussing how Jesus had gone back to Heaven. They spoke of the time when Christ would return from Heaven for all those who have received Him as their Savior.

"Paul, if Jesus came back today," said nine-year-old Debbie, "all the family would go to Heaven except you."

Paul burst into tears. "So you're going to leave me in the world?" he cried.

"Well, you can join us, and I'll help you do it," his father said kindly. Byang had a plan to help Paul understand. "Go out of the room, Paul," he instructed. "If you want to come in, knock on the door."

Paul went out, closed the door, and knocked. All was silent. He knocked again.

"Come in, Paul," Byang called. When Paul was back in the room, Byang explained that Jesus was knocking at his heart's door, wanting to come in and save him from his sins. "He is waiting for you to invite Him in," the father explained.

Paul understood at once. Bowing his head, he prayed, "I want You to come in, Lord Jesus. Thank you for shedding Your blood to take my punishment."

"Each member of my family is now a Christian," Byang said gratefully. He was thankful for the decision he had made to lead his family every day in Bible reading and prayer.

After going to America for further training, Byang became the leader of thousands of Bible-believing churches in Africa. He and his family moved across the African continent to the country of Kenya. From his home base in Nairobi, Kenya, Byang traveled throughout Africa and around the world, speaking to millions and writing about God's love. Some ten million African Christians looked up to him as their leader. From the time he was a boy, Byang Kato had made right decisions to follow God's leading, and throughout his life God strengthened him, honored him, and used him.

Nairobi (nī·rō′bē)

Time to Think

1. Did Byang's initiation into manhood bring him the happiness he longed for? What did?
2. Where did Byang get the money to attend a Christian college?
3. How did Byang decide whom he should marry?
4. What resulted from Byang's decision to lead his family in Bible study?
5. Why was God able to use Byang and bless him?

How the Dyaks Learned to Tithe

a true story from Borneo by Dr. J. Arthur Mouw (adapted)

It was hot in the jungle, and the tall grasses along the path whipped against the face of the missionary. Dr. Mouw hurried on, for he knew there would be many hundreds of Dyak Christians waiting for him under the shade of the big tree. But the Lord was speaking softly to his heart. "Why are you here?" He asked.

"Because Thou hast called me," answered the missionary.

"Why are you here?" Again the Lord spoke.

"Because, Lord, You said, 'Go into all the world and preach the gospel.' These people have never heard it, and that is why I came."

"Why are you here?" Once again the Lord spoke to the missionary.

Then Dr. Mouw knew what His Lord wanted to hear. He answered, "I am here because I love *You*."

As he hurried on, Dr. Mouw began to see that the Christian Dyaks on the island of Borneo were depending too much on him. God wanted Dr. Mouw to teach the Dyaks *how to live* and *how to give* so that they themselves could win their own people to Christ. He must give this message to the people waiting under the tree!

Dyaks (dī′ăks)   **Mouw** (mou)   **Borneo** (bôr′nē·ō′)

Dr. Mouw had four national helpers in Borneo. He went to them and said, "God's Word tells us that we are to give back to Him a tenth of what He gives to us. I believe God wants us to teach this to the Christian Dyaks."

But the national helpers said, "We cannot teach the Dyaks to give; they are too poor! If *you* believe in it, Dr. Mouw, *you* must be the one to teach it to them. We cannot take food from these hungry people."

Dr. Mouw knew how poor these people were. Much of the year they went hungry. All that they owned they could carry in their hands. They wore no clothes except clothes they made of bark, and the little boys and girls had no clothes at all!

But do you know *why* Dr. Arthur Mouw believed in tithing? Do you know *why* he believed that God wants us to give back to Him a tenth of all He gives us? It was because when he was a very little boy he had learned to tithe. He had given a tenth of his money to the Lord since he was eight years old. If he had a dime, he gave one penny to God. If he had a dollar, ten cents belonged to God. No matter how poor Arthur's parents were, they never used the tithe for themselves. And Arthur knew that God had taken care of them. They had never gone hungry.

So it came about that Dr. Mouw began to visit the meetings of the Christian Dyaks, going from village to village. He would hold his Bible high and say, "Everything I have taught you is from this Book. From it you have learned how the world was made. From it you have learned how sin came into the world. Best of all, you have learned from it how we are saved through the death of the Lord Jesus. Is this Book true?"

252

They answered as though with one great voice, "It is true; it has never lied to us."

"I am going to teach you something new today from this Book," said Dr. Mouw. "It is this: we are to give back to God a tenth of what He has given us. That means if you have ten chickens, one belongs to the Lord. If you have ten eggs, one belongs to the Lord. If you have ten cups of rice, one belongs to the Lord. God's Word tells us that He will give us everything we need and pour out a great blessing upon us if we will give Him a tenth."

The Dyak Christians sat quietly and thought! Then they spoke: "We have decided to do it God's way. He has done so much for us. We have been wishing that we had some way we could show our thanks to Him. This is a way. Three men will collect our gifts, and once each moon they will bring them to your home."

One day after the "new moon," or month, had arrived, Dr. and Mrs. Mouw heard a noise on their porch. There they met some Dyaks who had traveled for two days. And on the porch they found what they had brought. There were dozens of chickens, a high pile of cucumbers, a basketful of eggs, and many bags of rice. "This is God's part," the Dyaks said.

And each month it was the same. The porch was covered with food. Dr. Mouw was too happy to speak! He sold the food and bought nails, and they started to build churches for the Dyaks. When the next harvest time came, God sent the greatest rice crop the Dyaks had ever had.

And then, there was a great surprise at church! The Dyaks, who had never had any clothes but those made of bark now came to church dressed in comfortable clothes.

The itchy bark was gone, and instead they wore comfortable clothes made of cloth. When they had taken their extra rice to the store to sell, the merchant had told them, "It isn't good to go to church with bark clothes. Why don't you buy cloth and have comfortable clothes?"

The Dyaks built one church after another until there were fourteen! These churches were built because the Dyaks believed God's promise and began to tithe!

Time to Think

1. Why didn't the national helpers want to teach the Dyaks to tithe?
2. How did Dr. Mouw know God would provide for the Dyaks if they would tithe?
3. How did the Dyaks respond to Dr. Mouw's instruction on tithing?
4. Did the Dyaks tithe by putting money in the offering plate like we do?
5. How did the Dyaks know that they had done right by giving to the Lord?

The Bible
in Their Hearts

Grace W. McGavran

The sun was setting as Karl Olsen trudged through the mud of the scarcely passable road to Barren Village.

"These roads of East Poland!" he muttered crossly. "Almost impossible they are! If I were not carrying the Bible to people who do not have it, I would not wear myself out on them."

Karl was used to wearing himself out in such travel. On the muddy country roads, far back from towns and pavements, he often sank halfway to his knees in the bog holes. Usually he was cheerful enough about it, but sometimes after a long day of bad going he felt tired, and his good nature wore thin.

When he began to think that he could go no farther, and lamplighting time sent gleams of light from the tiny windows of villagers' homes, Karl came within sight of Barren Village. As he drew closer, dogs growled fiercely at him. But Karl had a way with dogs. Otherwise he would have been attacked and injured many a time.

He knocked at the door of the first house.

A man opened it and stood on the threshold, looking out. From under his arms three children peeked at the stranger who had appeared out of the gathering dusk.

"A welcome," said the man seriously. "Enter."

---

bog holes—*pits of mud or quicksand*   **threshold**—*the floor of a doorway*

But Karl did not come in. Not yet. "I am in search of a night's lodging, kind sir. I have money to pay for it and also for a meal. And I have a book from which to read stories. It has in it the most wonderful story the world has ever known."

Karl stood quietly waiting for the man to decide whether or not to take him in. Karl never pushed himself into people's homes. But usually one good look at his face won him a welcome.

"What say you, Marja?" The man addressed his wife. She came forward and examined Karl's face keenly.

"The night will be a bitter cold," she said. "We have room and there is enough food." She turned back to her stove.

"Come in, then. Come in and warm yourself. I bear the name of Antoni Kowalski. And yours?"

"Karl Olsen," said the other. "I carry books to sell. I also read and tell stories to those in whose homes I lodge."

The children clustered around Karl as he seated himself by the big tiled stove that stood high at the side of the room.

Little Marja, named for her mother, and the oldest of the three children, smiled shyly at Karl. "A story?" she begged. Her father laughed.

"Never has little Marja had enough stories," he said. "But let our guest get his hands warm, child, before you pester him."

Karl was soon warm and comfortable. He opened his pack and took out a Bible.

Marja (mä′rē·ə)
Antoni Kowalski (än′taw′nē kō·wäl′skē)

"Here it is, the most precious Book in the world. Shall I read you a story from it? Here is a story told by Jesus to the people who gathered around him."

Karl opened the Bible. He read the story of the Good Samaritan. "You have been good Samaritans to me," he said. "You have taken me in and sheltered me. From the dark roadway and the danger of animals that would do me harm you have saved me."

Then it was time for supper. Karl enjoyed the hot food. The meal was simple peasant fare, but it was well prepared and strengthening.

Afterwards Marja and Antoni and little Marja and Jan and Zosia sat and listened while Karl told them story after story.

He told them about Joseph and David. He told of Solomon's building the beautiful temple, and of Daniel's being thrown into the den of lions. Before telling each story, he opened the Bible to the right chapter. As he talked, he would read a verse here and there, to put that part of the story into the exact words of the Bible.

Little Marja sighed with pleasure as Karl finally closed the Book. "Let us buy a Bible so that Father can read from it every evening," she begged. "Father is the only one in the village who can read," she explained proudly to Karl.

"We are too poor for books." Her father frowned.

"Those without this Book are poor," said Karl softly. "But those who have it, possess that which is better than riches."

Jan (yän)   **Zosia** (zō′syə)

"Please! Please!" begged little Marja. Finally her father
yielded and bought the Bible. He set it in a place of honor in
the house.

Karl stayed with the family for two days. He made
friends with others in the village, but no one else would buy a
Bible, or a New Testament, or even a Gospel. Karl was disappointed. It had meant so much to him to find, on the very
night he arrived, a family ready to buy the whole Bible. He
had hoped there would be others in Barren Village who
would buy.

On the third day Karl left to go on to other towns and
villages. As he plodded through the thick mud of the road,
he kept thinking about how little he had sold.

"Ah well," said he to himself, "it is true that I go away from this place, but the Word of God remains behind. There is now a Bible in Barren Village where there was none before. And who knows what may happen?"

Winter came to East Poland, and long, long evenings when the sun set early and wolves roamed the countryside. No one stirred much from home, and there was little to do within.

On such evenings Antoni would take down the Bible and read the stories that Karl had marked. He would read the teachings of Jesus from the chapters and verses that Karl had listed for him.

As he read aloud, Marja and little Marja and Jan and Zosia sat around and listened. Afterwards they would talk about what they had heard and wonder at it.

Sometimes a neighbor would come in. Antoni would reach for the Bible and say, "Listen to a thing I have found in this Book. Listen well and tell me what you think of such teaching."

He would read while the neighbor sat with head on one side, listening carefully. Then would come argument and conversation about the meaning of the teaching. The talk would be about what they themselves should do. The children would drink in the thoughts that were being discussed.

"Why should I forgive my enemy?" the neighbor would inquire. "Does the Book mean that I should chop wood for someone who stole part of my wheat crop? Surely it cannot mean that!"

"Who knows? It would be a strange way to act." And Antoni would shake his head doubtfully. "A strange teaching."

"Or this now—" and he would turn to another verse— "Do unto others as you would have them do unto you."

Little Marja and Jan listened as their father and one neighbor or another talked. They heard the teaching about doing as one would be done by discussed over and over again. They would look at each other and remember that when they were playing with other children they had not always acted in that kindly way.

How the change came about no one could tell, because it was all so slow that no one noticed what was happening until things were different. "Like yeast, working silently in dough,"

Jesus had said, when he talked about God's spirit at work in the hearts of men. And so it was in Barren Village. The teachings of God's Word began to change Antoni and his family and his neighbors and their friends and the way they thought and talked and acted. Barren Village began to blossom with kind thoughts and good deeds.

There came the day when Antoni and Marja and little Marja and Jan became followers of Jesus, not only in their hearts, but openly, before others. Zosia was too young to become a church member, but she, too, loved Jesus and tried to act as a child of God should.

Then others of the villagers found that they, too, wanted to be of the company of those who are called Christians.

One day Antoni and Marja made a count of those in Barren Village who were now followers of Christ. "One hundred ninety-eight, one hundred ninety-nine, two hundred," they counted. "If only Karl could know how much has come to this village from the one Bible he left here!"

It was the fact that they had just one Bible that began to worry the two hundred Christians of Barren Village. "Why did we not buy the Book when Karl was here?" they mourned. "Why did we let him carry away those precious copies?" But it was too late now to regret what had happened.

"Suppose Antoni's house should burn down," they worried. "What if a thief came in when all of us were working in the fields and stole our only Bible?"

"I know some of it by heart," said little Marja. "I know the story of Jesus and the children, and the Hundredth Psalm."

"I know the story of the Good Samaritan," said Jan. "I can say it without a mistake."

"My heart is full of many small verses that I have loved," offered Marja, "but I do not know any chapter from one end to the next."

That gave everyone an idea. "We must learn the whole Bible," decided the two hundred Christians. "We must learn it by heart. Every part of it that we can possibly learn we will memorize."

So they made a plan. They first listed the verses and the chapters and the stories and the passages that they most loved and that had the teachings they thought were most important.

Then each person was given something to learn. The little children learned verses. The older children learned stories and short passages and psalms that were not too long. The grownups took the hard parts of the Bible to learn. They worked and worked on the memorizing.

Sometimes the Christians would get together and someone would start with the opening of the first chapter of a book, such as the Gospel of Luke. He would recite as far as his part went. Then the person who had the next part would stand and repeat his. Antoni would hold the Bible in his hand and follow the recitation to be sure it was correct, word for word. On and on would go the reciting. Each one knew where his part fitted into the whole.

The long winter evenings were busy now with reading and repeating and memorizing. It was surprising how much of the Bible was learned that first winter. And during the next two years still more was memorized.

The sun was setting one day as Karl Olsen trudged through the mud of the scarcely passable road to Barren Village. "Years ago," he was thinking, "I visited this place so far from everywhere. I sold but one copy of the Bible there. I sold it to the man in whose house I stayed. Now what was his name?" And Karl tried to dig out of his memory the name of Antoni. At last it came, for Karl had a good memory for names. He was glad. It was always pleasant to greet people by name. It was a pleasure to him and to the one whose name he had remembered.

As lamplighting time sent little gleams of light from the tiny windows of the village houses, Karl came once more to the door of Antoni and Marja. He knocked, wondering if they still lived there and if the three children were all still alive and well.

Little Marja came to the door this time. She was taller than her mother now and had grown older. After a moment's looking at the stranger who stood before her, Marja remembered him. She called out in delight, "Karl! Mama! Mama! It is Karl, come back after all these years!"

The family crowded around him then—Antoni and big Marja and Jan and Zosia. Word went flying around the village that Karl had come, and in a flash others were there, smiling and welcoming him.

Karl was confused beyond measure. Why such a greeting? How did they happen to remember him?

Little by little the story came out. Antoni produced the Bible, so worn that it was nearly ready to fall apart. Marja, interrupted a hundred times by others eager to join in the telling, told him how they had studied the teachings and how two hundred and more of the people of Barren Village had become followers of Jesus. But no one thought to tell Karl about learning the Bible by heart. That was something they had done for their own sakes and it did not occur to them that what they had done would be of interest to anyone else.

Next day they gathered for worship and Karl was with them. During the service he asked, hoping to get at least a few responses, "Shall we then, repeat from memory some of the verses we have come to love? Is there someone here who has learned a verse and would like to recite it?"

There was a moment's silence. Then Antoni asked, "Verses, or chapters?"

Karl looked as amazed and delighted as he felt. "Chapters!" He asked, "Is there anyone here who knows a whole chapter of the Bible by heart?"

They told him then of how they had been seized with fear of losing their only Bible, and of how they had memorized it, chapter after long chapter, each taking a share. "Almost the whole Bible is learned, and we are working now on the parts that are yet to be committed to memory," they told him with pride.

Jan recited and little Marja, and Zosia and all the other children, verse after verse and chapter after chapter. The minutes sped by. The older people recited some of the chapters they liked best.

Karl stayed in Barren Village for a week. The Christians, so far from all other Christians, had many questions to ask him. They bought all the copies of the Bible and of the New Testament and of the Gospels that he had with him.

"We have the Bible in our hearts," they said, "but no one of us has more than a small portion of the whole of it. And each of us needs it all."

"God's Word worked in the hearts and minds of the people here," thought Karl to himself as he lay in bed the night before he was to leave. "Only one copy of the Bible and see what has come of it!"

Time to Think

1. What convinced Antoni to buy a Bible from Karl?
2. Were the Kowalski family Christians when they began reading the Bible? When did they become Christians?
3. What made the 200 Christians begin memorizing the Bible?
4. What lessons can we learn from the people of Barren Village?

The Best of All

Fanny Crosby

Although she probably never saw a Bible, Fanny Crosby had such a deep love for God's Word that she memorized long portions of it as a child. With the Bible in her heart, blind Fanny Crosby was enabled by God to write some of America's favorite hymns, including "Blessed Assurance," "Near the Cross," and "To God Be the Glory." In this poem she expresses her great reverence for God's Word.

Blessed Bible, sacred treasure,
    Precious Book, of all the best,
There is comfort never failing,
    And a calm abiding rest.
Read with reverence, and commit it,
    Verse by verse, and day by day;
'Tis the word that God has spoken,
    And it cannot pass away.

reverence—*utmost respect*   **sacred**—*holy*   **commit**—*memorize*

Glossary

Pronunciation Key

Symbol ▪ Example		Symbol ▪ Example	
ā	āte	ô	côrd, taught, saw
â	dâre	ŏ	nŏt
ă	făt	oi	boil
ä	fäther	o͞o	bro͞od
ə	ago (ə·gō′)	o͝o	bo͝ok
ch	chin	ou	out
ē	ēven	sh	shark
ĕ	ĕgg	th	thin
*ȇ (ər)	pondȇr	t̶h̶	t̶h̶ere
g	good	*tu̯ (cho͞o)	virtu̯e
ī	īce	ū	ūnit
ĭ	ĭt	û	ûrn
j	jog	ŭ	ŭp
ks	perplex (ks = x)	zh	azure (zh = z)
kw	quart (kw = qu)	’	little (lĭt′’l; shows that the vowel is not sounded)
ng	song		
ō	ōver		

*Note: For simplicity, the alternate symbols are used for ȇr and tu̯.

Abbreviation Key

adj. adjective   *adv.* adverb   *n.* noun   *v.* verb

*This glossary contains words from the stories in this book.
The meaning given here fits the word the first time it is used.
Use your regular dictionary to find meanings of other words
you find difficult or to find other meanings for the words here.*

A

adamant (ăd'ə·mənt) *adj.* stubborn and unwilling to yield

allurement (ə·lŏŏr'mənt) *n.* attraction

aloft (ə·lôft') *adv.* up in the air

amiss (ə·mĭs') *adv.* not as planned

anesthetic (ăn'ĭs·thĕt'ĭk) *n.* medicine that numbs pain

ardent (är'd'nt) *adj.* full of strong feeling or devotion

arid (ăr'ĭd) *adj.* dry

astir (ə·stûr') *adj.* full of motion

at bay (ăt bā) *adv.* back at a safe distance

B

bandits (băn'dĭts) *n.* thieves with guns

belike (bĭ·līk') *adv.* probably

bickering (bĭk'ər·ĭng) *v.* disagreeing needlessly

billy club (bĭl'ē clŭb) *n.* a short, thick stick carried for protection

boarding houses (bôrd'ĭng hou'zĭz) *n.* houses where rooms can be rented

bog holes (bôg hōlz) *n.* pits of mud or quicksand

buttes (byōōts) *n.* hills that have flat tops

C

call to arms (kôl tə ärmz) *n.* announcement to prepare to fight

cannery (kăn'ə·rē) *n.* a factory where food is put into cans

capers (kā'pərz) *n.* playful acts

ceiling (sē'lĭng) *n.* the maximum height at which one can fly under normal conditions

civil (sĭv'əl) *adj.* polite; socially acceptable

clime (klīm) *n.* climate

clout (klout) *n.* a powerful blow

commit (kə·mĭt') *v.* memorize

condescending (kŏn'dĭ·sĕn'dĭng) *adj.* having an air of superiority

congregated (kŏng'grĭ·gāt·ĕd) *v.* gathered

conies (kō'nēz) *n.* small furry animals similar to rabbits

convention (kən·vĕn'shən) *n.* a large meeting

convoying (kŏn'voi·ĭng) *v.* escorting; leading along

courting (kôrt'ĭng) *v.* trying to win another's affection

creed (krēd) *n.* a statement of what one believes

crest (krĕst) *n.* the very top

cultivated (kŭl'tə·vāt·ĕd) *v.* prepared for growth

currants (kûr′ənts) *n.* dried berries, much like raisins

cygnets (sĭg′nĭts) *n.* baby swans

D

defile (dĭ·fīl′) *n.* a narrow passageway

desolate (dĕs′ə·lĭt) *adj.* deserted

desolation (dĕs·ə·lā′shən) *n.* destruction

detaining (dĭ·tān′ĭng) *v.* holding back

dinars (dĭ·närz′) *n.* coins

dire (dīr) *adj.* extreme

disembark (dĭs′ĕm·bärk′) *v.* to get off a ship

disillusionment (dĭs′ĭ·lōō′zhən·mənt) *n.* disappointment

docile (dŏs′əl) *adj.* easily taught

doxology (dŏk·sŏl′ə·jē) *n.* a short hymn of praise

drone (drōn) *n.* a low continuous sound

E

elements (ĕl′ə·mənts) *n.* weather

eligible (ĕl′ĭ·jə·bəl) *adj.* qualified

eloquent (ĕl′ə·kwənt) *adj.* able to persuade by speech

enthralled (ĕn·thrôld′) *adj.* completely attentive

erect (ĭ·rĕkt′) *adj.* straight up

escapades (ĕs′kə·pādz′) *n.* adventures

exhibit (ĭg·zĭb′ĭt) *n.* a display

F

feeble (fē′bəl) *adj.* weak

fife (fīf) *n.* a small flute

flax (flăks) *n.* plant stems used to make cloth

flint (flĭnt) *n.* a hard rock used to spark a fire

forsythia (fôr·sĭth′ē·ə) *n.* yellow flowers

frigidity (frĭ·jĭd′ĭ·tē) *n.* extreme cold

G

gallant (găl′ənt) *adj.* brave and noble

gamely (gām′lē) *adv.* without yielding

gaped (gāpt) *v.* stared with an open mouth

general missionary (jĕn′ər·əl mĭsh′ən·ĕr′ē) *n.* a representative who travels from church to church

gilded (gĭld′ĕd) *adj.* trimmed in gold

goad (gōd) *n.* a pointed rod used to urge animals along

gold bug (gōld bŭg) *n.* a beetle having a gold color

gorge (gôrj) *n.* a deep passage with rock walls

greenhorn (grēn′hôrn′) *n.* a newcomer

H

hedgehog (hĕj′hôg′) *n.* a small animal similar to a porcupine

heed (hēd) *v.* pay attention to

Hessians (hĕsh′ənz) *n.* German soldiers

hoisted (hoist′ĕd) *v.* raised or put up

homage (hŏm′ĭj) *n.* special honor and respect

I

idyllic (ī·dĭl′ĭk) *adj.* simple

illuminated (ĭ·lōō′mə·nāt′ĕd) *v.* lit up

incensed (ĭn·sĕnst′) *adj.* very angry

incessantly (ĭn·sĕs′ənt·lē) *adv.* without stopping

incinerator (ĭn·sĭn′ə·rā′tər) *n.* an appliance used to burn trash

inclement (ĭn·klĕm′ənt) *adj.* stormy

initiation (ĭ·nĭsh′ē·ā′shən) *n.* the act or ceremony that permits membership in a group

intoxicated (ĭn·tŏk′sĭ·kāt′ĭd) *adj.* excited

intrigued (ĭn·trēgd′) *adj.* interested

intuitively (ĭn·tōō′ĭ·tĭv·lē) *adv.* by instinct

irksome (ûrk′səm) *adj.* annoying

K

kimono (kə·mō′nə) *n.* a loose robe worn by Japanese women

L

landscapes (lănd′scāps′) *n.* paintings of scenery

lee (lē) *n.* the side protected from the wind

litter (lĭt′ər) *n.* a seat mounted on poles carried by servants

loam (lōm) *n.* soil

locust (lō′kəst) *n.* a type of grasshopper

lurching (lûrch′ĭng) *v.* moving forward uncertainly

M

malice (măl′ĭs) *n.* anger

Martinique (mär′tə·nēk′) *n.* an island in the West Indies

monarch (mŏn′ərk) *n.* a king or queen

muskie (mŭs′kē) *n.* a large fish caught for food

muster (mŭs′tər) *v.* gather

mutually (myōō′chōō·ə·lē) *adv.* in agreement with each other

N

negotiations (nĭ·gō′shē·ā′shənz) *n.* discussions held in order to reach a decision

nuisances (nōō′səns·ĕz) *n.* things that annoy

O

onerous (ŏn′ər·əs) *adj.* troublesome

orator (ôr′ə·tər) *n.* speaker

ordinances (ôr′d′n·əns·ĕz) *n.* regulations set by the government

ores (ôrz) *n.* minerals that contain metal

P

Palisades (păl′ĭ·sādz′) *n.* a row of steep cliffs along the bank of the Hudson River

partition (pär·tĭsh′ən) *n.* something that divides a room into sections

patent (păt′′nt) *n.* an official document that states the rights of an owner

pell-mell (pĕl′mĕl′) *adv.* in a frantic, confused manner

philosophically (fĭl′ə·sŏf′ĭ·kəl·ē) *adv.* relying on reason and wisdom

pilgrimage (pĭl′grə·mĭj) *n.* a journey to visit a shrine

pincers (pĭn′sərz) *n.* large tongs with jawlike ends

pluck (plŭk) *n.* courage in time of difficulty

politic (pŏl′ĭ·tĭk) *adj.* having to do with civil government

profound (prə·found′) *adj.* of great importance

propel (prə·pĕl′) *v.* push forward

propose (prə·pōz′) *v.* to give an idea

prudent (prōōd′′nt) *adj.* having common sense; practical

R

ramparts (răm′pärts′) *n.* forts

ratify (răt′ə·fī′) *v.* approve

ravine (rə·vēn′) *n.* a deep valley caused by water

reef (rēf) *n.* a ridge of rock or coral in a body of water

rendition (rĕn·dĭsh′ən) *n.* a performance

repealed (rĭ·pēld′) *v.* taken away

reprieve (rĭ·prēv′) *n.* cancellation of punishment

reverence (rĕv′ər·əns) *n.* utmost respect

rill (rĭl) *n.* a small stream

riots (rī′əts) *n.* angry displays by large crowds

rites (rīts) *n.* ceremonies

rogues (rōgz) *n.* people who cause trouble

rove (rōv) *v.* to move about freely

S

sacred (sā′krĭd) *adj.* holy

safeguards (sāf′gärds) *n.* things that protect

sage (sāj) *n.* a fragrant plant whose leaves are used in cooking

scoffer (skŏf′ər) *n.* someone who mocks

scrub (skrŭb) *n.* a short bush

scythe (sīth) *n.* a curved blade used for reaping

sentinel duty (sĕn′tə·nəl dōō′tē) *n.* guard duty

sentry (sĕn′trē) *n.* a guard placed in a certain spot to keep people from passing

serene (sə·rēn′) *adj.* still and quiet

Shinto (shĭn′tō) *n.* a Japanese religion

shrine (shrīn) *n.* a place where offerings are made to idols

sickle (sĭk′əl) *n.* a curved blade used for cutting grain

spinning jenny (spĭn′ĭng jĕ′nē) *n.* a machine used to spin thread

spire (spīr) *n.* a structure that goes to a point at the top

spontaneous (spŏn·tā′nē·əs) *adj.* not planned

staunch (stônch) *adj.* not moving

steerage (stĭr′ĭj) *n.* the section of the ship that has the cheapest rooms

stucco (stŭk′ō) *n.* thick plaster

studied (stŭ′dēd) *adj.* learned and thought about

suave (swäv) *adj.* agreeable

subjects (sŭb′jĭkts) *n.* people under a ruler's authority

submit (səb·mĭt′) *v.* to present as an option

subsistence rations (sŭb·sĭs′təns ră′shənz) *n.* just enough food to stay alive

T

threshes (thrĕsh′ĕz) *v.* separates grain and seed from straw

threshold (thrĕsh′ōld) *n.* the floor of a doorway

treacherous (trĕch′ər·əs) *adj.* dangerous

tributaries (trĭb′yə·tĕr′ēz) *n.* streams that flow into a larger body of water

tyrant (tī′rənt) *n.* a cruel ruler

U

undertook (ŭn′dər·tŏok′) *v.* agreed to do

unicorn (yōo′nĭ·kôrn) *n.* a fictional animal usually pictured as a horse with one horn in the center of its head

V

vales (vālz) *n.* valleys

vigil (vĭj′əl) *n.* a time of watching

W

welfare (wĕl′fâr′) *n.* the condition

wily (wī′lē) *adj.* sly; full of tricks

Y

yen (yĕn) *n.* a Japanese coin

Credits

Photos/illustrations: iii—Digital Stock; iv—Digital Stock; v—Corel; 64—"Signing the Mayflower Compact," J. L. G. Ferris/William Ryder; 91—original of the "Spirit of '76" by Archibald Willard hangs in the Selectmen's Meeting Room, Marblehead, Massachusetts; 114–115—sky Digital Stock; 172—mountains Digital Stock, Statue of Liberty A Beka Book, White House Corel; 173—all Corel.

"Bambi Finds the Meadow" reprinted with the permission of Simon & Schuster and Simon & Schuster Books for Young Readers from *Bambi* by Felix Salten. Copyright 1928 Simon & Schuster Inc.; copyright ©1956 Simon & Schuster Inc. Also by permission of Jonathan Cape, publisher.

"The Bible in Their Hearts," "The Bible Rides the Western Plains," "The Little Slave Girl of Madagascar," and "When the Morning Star Sailed" in *Stories of the Book of Books* by Grace W. McGavran. ©1947 by Friendship Press. Used by permission.

"The Book from the Street" from *Stories of Yesterday and Today for Juniors,* 1961, Abingdon Press, used by permission of Edith Kelsey Lewis.

"Boots and the Cat" by Kitsi Gumensky ©1934 Rand McNally in *Child Life Magazine.* All rights reserved; reprinted by permission of Rand McNally.

Excerpt from "Children of the Wind" in *The People, Yes* by Carl Sandburg, copyright 1936 by Harcourt Brace & Company and renewed 1964 by Carl Sandburg, reprinted by permission of the publisher.

"The Decisions of Byang Kato" (originally "Five Big Choices") ©1980 by Child Evangelism Fellowship. All rights reserved. Used by permission.

"The Fox and the Grapes" from *The Golden Treasury of Poetry,* by Joseph Lauren, selected by Louis Untermeyer; ©1959 Golden Books Publishing Company Inc. All rights reserved. Used by permission.

"Frisbie Cures the Doctor" from *'Teens,* The American Baptist Publication Society, used by permission of Judson Press.

"How the Dyaks Learned to Tithe" copyright ©1983 by Child Evangelism Fellowship Inc. All rights reserved. Used by permission.

"Meeting," copyright 1926 by Doubleday, a division of Bantam, Doubleday, Dell Publishing Group, Inc. from *Taxis and Toadstools* by Rachel Field. Used by permission of Bantam Doubleday Dell Books for Young Readers and Egmont Children's Books Ltd.

"Missionary Call" taken from *Jan Ken Pon* by Patricia Finrow Clark. Copyright ©1961 Moody Bible Institute of Chicago, Moody Press. Used by permission.

276